Photograph: Ruth McDonald

Connecting Nothing With Something

A Coastal Anthology

Influx Press, London

Published by Influx Press
Studio 25, The Heartspace
Hackney Downs Studio, Amhurst Terrace
London, E8 2BT
www.influxpress.com

Introduction and selection © Kit Caless and Gary Budden 2013

First published 2013.

Printed and bound in the UK by the Short Run Press Ltd.,
Exeter.

ISBN 978-0-9571693-6-4

Dearest Meghan

you'd be in the dedication
but we didn't do one
So check the acknowledgments!

I love you

Kit

Contents

IV - Hastings

V - Into Sussex

Foreword

Travis Elborough

Dreamland Welcomes You, runs the sign on Margate's currently derelict amusement park. Its name, that mix of terra firma and fantasy, sums up the collisions to be found in most seaside resorts. They are places, after all, where the usual distinctions between the earth and the sea, work and play, the past and the present, the end and the beginning and myth and reality, fact and fiction, shift as constantly as the tide. Even the air, choppy, damp and heavy with salt, can never be trusted entirely.

Such a perfidious terrain, augmented as it is by a few centuries of building heavily weighted to either repelling the sea or providing relaxation and out and out pleasure, needs careful consideration. The sea itself may well be sublime – in the true sense of the word. But the seaside can often border on the ridiculous with its rusty windmill-strewn crazy golf courses and Brobdingnagian plastic ice cream cones. That contrast, though, is also a deep seated part of the appeal. To me, at least. While the post-package holiday slide of towns like Folkestone, Margate and Hastings into decay and even ruination – for years practically an off-the-shelf metaphor for the nation itself and difficult to enjoy close at hand – has left them with a uniquely faded, out of time, glamour. A quality that for over a decade now has held a special allure to former urban scavengers priced out of London, or jaded by its endemic homogenization and expensification. Shoreditch is busy being reborn on the seaside, Hoxton has come to Hastings, with art galleries and vintage shops selling old stuff like new.

But then, south coast resorts have always been parasites of the capital in one way or another. Back when Brighton was Brighthelmstone and still a scrofulous fishing port awaiting the Prince Regent's midas touch, the bulk of its daily catch went up to Billingsgate. Boats called 'hoys' and carrying cockneys from London on the Thames to the Kent coast were the making of Margate, Ramsgate and Herne Bay, turning royal watering retreats into popular bathing resorts. In fact, until they were taken down after the North Sea flood of 1953, the balustrades from Old London Bridge lined the entrance to Herne Bay Pier. Two stone alcoves from that selfsame bridge, meanwhile, were used to furnish Victoria Park in Hackney with shelters. Its replacement inspired and appeared in T S Eliot's *The Wasteland*, partly written on the front in Margate. This coast. That city.

It's all about making the right connections, isn't it? Nothing with something. You'll see.

Introduction

Gary Budden

There's a kind of navel-gazing that can arise from living in a city like London, something that manifests itself in the writing we create and consume. As a place (world famous and justly worthy of a lifetime's exploration) that had defined my twenties, it was understandable how the city would exert influence on its writers.

The first Influx Press project took this single-minded obsession and fascination to an extreme; not a book about London as a whole, but one that focused merely on one of its constituent boroughs, Hackney (*Acquired for Development By . . .*) This was a place that had had massive impact on my adult life, a place in constant flux and a useful microcosm to illuminate and explore the big issues of gentrification, regeneration, housing, the social effects of late neo-liberal capitalism and shifting demographics that have largely dominated the cultural discourse of the last decade. We live in a world of blink-and-you-miss-it redevelopment, unstable geographies where the signifiers and signposts of where you are change with an alarming frequency. Nothing is stable and that ominous process, progress, is in constant motion.

There is another story, though. There always is. We'd done our Hackney book, got a lot of it out of our system, addressed and highlighted a few problems, and exorcised some ghosts. We even sold a few books.

Kit Caless and I, the editors of this book , both grew up in Kent in the 80s and 90s. It is a place we are – for obvious reasons – still very much attached too whether we like it or not. Family. Friends. More importantly, memories, and those formative and indelible experiences that mark a person in their early years that are impossible to shake; even a denial, a disavowal of the unfashionable place you originate from, is to be defined by it in some way.

Although I was born on the fringes of London near Wembley, (another deeply unfashionable landscape, made transcendent through the work of Nick Papadimitriou and his book *Scarp*), I grew up from the age of two in the fishing town of Whitstable, on the north Kent coast looking out over the Thames estuary. It's a place that has begun to feature heavily in my own writing, a re-appreciation of a place I once thought deathly dull and couldn't wait to escape from. An obvious and perhaps clichéd sign of getting older, but true nonetheless. These days I find the sea a reassuring constant (I would discover, investigating the Cinque Ports, how the sea can even disappear).

I have clear memories of daytrips along the coast to Margate, to ride the rides at Bembom Brothers / Dreamland (a name that was asking for trouble if ever there were one), my dad talking about unfathomable lost tribes with names like mods, rockers, skinheads, punks. There were sandy picnic days in Broadstairs and my mother, not yet an English teacher, talking about someone called Charles Dickens and a place called Bleak House. This was all before the taste for irony had taken root. Our visits lacked inverted commas; people genuinely took their children to these towns for fun, a day out. Listen to Chas and Dave, dip into the BFIs archive or watch the film adaptation of Graham Swift's *Last Orders* if you want to find some proof of that. The idea that you could enjoy a place ironically has never really sat well with me; you either enjoy it or you don't. Margate can never be ironic to me; my dad and my brother work there helping vulnerable young people, dealing with the reality of the place. Using it as background wallpaper to set my fashionably-unfashionable daytrips against would be an insult.

My dad, a keen birdwatcher and self-taught ornithologist, helped bring the Kent and Sussex coasts alive (perhaps I was bored at the time, now I'm grateful for these trips). Binocular and wellington jaunts to Dungeness, Romney Marsh, Rye, the white cliffs of Dover, somewhere near Hastings (Battle?), Pegwell Bay. Know how to look at a place and it becomes wondrous; realize you're not just anywhere, but somewhere specific with its own set of rules.

Later, late 90s now, I'd travel with friends to Margate to see touring punk and post-hardcore bands play in the anachronistic surroundings of the Margate Lido (I'd selectively delete my history of seeing The Levellers at the Winter Gardens). Back then, regeneration was a foreign concept to me, global capitalism not a notion I would entertain until I saw *Fight Club* in Canterbury, 1999. I remember us running fast back along the seafront to make the last train, through salty drizzle, past hulking bouncers, bored prostitutes, everyone, like ourselves, drunk. These are not negative memories; I loved it, without irony.

Then I left Kent for university, left university for London, and I didn't visit these places for many years. Sucked, like so many, into the city. At somepoint in this era, we'd travel to Camber Sands for the ATP Festival, chalets from another era housing, temporarily, fans of achingly cool music that was completely *now* (that was then).

On 16th April 2011, the Turner Contemporary opened its

doors in Margate. The Christmas of that year I was in Kent for family visits, and my dad asked if I wanted to join him to see an exhibition at the Turner entitled 'Nothing in the World but Youth'. I went with not the highest of hopes, a provincial art gallery with debated benefits for the town it inhabited, Margate in the dead of winter, wandering around an art gallery with my father (who, it is fair to say, doesn't really do that kind of thing). I was surprised. A fascinating exhibition detailing all kinds of youth movements from the nineteenth century onwards. What most struck me was a striking wall display of fliers, zines, patches, badges and other ephemera from the punk, anarchist, skinhead, post-punk (and even neo-Nazi) scenes of the 70s and 80s and how some of this directly tied to Margate and the Kent coast. As someone with a heavy interest in, and a strong involvement with, these scenes (not the fascist ones . . .), it was inevitable that I would be grabbed by this.

It set off thoughts of gigs at the Lido in a different century, violent clashes on London streets, a beating from police the day Tomlinson died, curlews and sandpipers flitting on the Kent coast, daytrips to the now-boarded up Dreamland (a bad metaphor, unforgiveable if you dreamed it up in fiction – you'd be laughed out of the writers' club).

I was at an exhibition that genuinely interested me; that was a revelation in itself. The fact I was looking at old Conflict posters and National Front totenkopfs in a Tate gallery, in *Margate* of all places, sent my thoughts spinning off in all directions. It seemed deeply symbolic, though of what I couldn't have said at that exact moment. The past felt alive.

This experience became, in heavily fictionalised form, *The Exhibition*, my contribution to this anthology of coastal writing, *Connecting Nothing with Something*. It kick-started me into thinking about the hidden histories and counter-narratives that exist all over the country, even out here on England's half-forgotten periphery. It knocked me out of my London navel-gazing.

The very fact I was presented with this deluge of sub-cultural information in the managed space of a Tate gallery, itself attempting to codify and understand the messiness of history, put me on the path to knowing that this was really a place worthy of exploration. And not just Margate; the whole stretch from Kent into East Sussex, all the 180 degree towns forever defined by the sea (or even a lack of sea, like Sandwich and Romney Marsh). And asking around friends, colleagues, other writers, it became clear that others were also interested in these issues.

The title, as most reading this will probably know, is an adaptation from a line in TS Eliot's *The Wasteland*. We are more hopeful.

Compiling this short anthology, the affect of the sea on the psyche became immediately noticeable. The sheer age of this small country is more vivid and oppressive in such places – but also thrilling if you allow it. The coast invites reverie and reflection whereas London inspires urgency, anger, anxiety.

The stories and poems contained here, through no conscious action on the part of the editors, are more contemplative, thoughtful, melancholy and less angry than our book of Hackney writing. The act of staring out to the sea, an uncluttered view unimpeded by buildings in various states of degeneration or completion, changes the mood. Turn around, see towns in need of help, boarded up shops sitting next to the first stirring signs of gentrification. New art galleries with gulls resting on their roofs. Boutique shops, charity shops. New tourists, either attempting to reclaim the seaside holidays of their childhoods or an ironic quest for an authentic experience. Places quintessentially English, yet stuck out on the edge of the country. We know, somewhere over the waves, France lurks.

The pieces contained in this book are from, as with *Acquired for Development By* . . . , a diverse array of writers all with some connection to the coasts of Kent and Sussex. For whatever reason, the majority of work we received focused on the towns of Margate and Hastings. The two places appear to exert a particular hold over the imagination. And, perhaps coincidence, perhaps not, they are excellent examples in motion of the current attempt to start regenerating the coastal towns through art, with the opening of Turner Contemporary in Margate and the Jerwood Gallery in Hastings. Whether this works or not is yet to be seen; I am not a dour cynic and I don't write it all off. Clearly we, as writers and producers of books, believe that the creative arts can have a positive impact on people's lives. As always, an anthology such as this could not, and does not, attempt to have any final say on the issues we are touching on. These are personal and creative takes on this landscape from a group of excellent and diverse writers, and I am excited and proud to be publishing the work of such a talented group of people.

Kit Caless

I have left Kent many times.

In the summer of 2001 I used to leave three times a day, in fact, on a P&O ferry called The Canterbury. Sometimes at night, more often in the bright light of a midsummer sun.

I cycled from my family home in a small village called Barham, thirteen miles to Dover. I rode along back roads dappled with light through woodland trees, past tiny primary schools, country pubs and downhill towards the sea. On the boat I worked in the canteen, the mess, the games room, the deck – all over. Each time we set sail, I would run up to the deck and watch the ferry depart the port, leaving the iconic white cliffs to get smaller and smaller.

Every time we returned, I would stay inside hoping we would never arrive back at the port. I would wish that we would dock somewhere else, not Dover, not Kent.

By the time I was old enough to work on those ferries, escaping Kent had become an obsession. Being so close to the coast, so close to France and the continent developed the gnawing idea that there was always something better, somewhere else.

Unable to afford to leave the country for most of my adolescence, trains frequently took me to London and back. We snuck into clubs underage, we dug in record store crates, we dreamed the dreams of youth on the banks of the Thames, pretending this city would be ours when we came of age. Then came a bit more money, cheaper flights abroad and the lure of escape to far continents. I wanted to be as far away from Kent as possible. I had learned how to leave in Dover and felt the urge to put this into extreme practice.

I tried pretty hard to go pretty far.

I ended up at one point in 2007, walking into a bar in Lima, Peru. I don't think I'd seen the yellow sands of Jos Bay or the winding Valley Road for at least three years by then. Kent was far behind me. A memory, distant, unchanging.

I'd spent the day looking for somewhere that might possibly have a television that would be screening the England-India test match. Most mention of cricket on the streets of Lima drew a blank, but one man told me there was a cricket club in San Isidro. On arrival, a few old gentlemen walked past me in whites carrying Newberry cricket bats, nodded their heads and talked passionately about tactics – combining Spanish sentences with English field placings. I found the reception and asked if they had DirecTV and if they had bought the rights to screen the match. The lady behind the desk shook her head. No, she said, but there is an English pub by the cricket pitch if I'd like to have a look.

I thanked her and headed in the direction of the 'pub'. I felt discombobulated enough being in a cricket club in Lima, but to arrive at The Cricketers, set back behind the pavilion was extraordinary. The pub was a replica of a stereotypical Kentish pub. Hops (probably fake) lined the wooden beams above the bar. The chairs were solid, upholstered with a dark green check, the tables deep oak, soaked in beer stains. At the pumps, no Shepherd Neame (unfortunately) but at least some form of ale. The spirits were gins, rums and vodkas. There was a dartboard and, quite unbelievably, a bat and trap set resting against the wall in the far corner. I hadn't seen bat and trap outside of Kent, let alone on the far side of the world.

I ordered a gin and tonic and chatted to the bar tender. He knew nothing about the bat and trap, or about Kent. He said he liked cricket but couldn't play very well. I bored him with stories of games down in Bishopsbourne and against Dover Grammar,

Kwick Cricket at the St Lawrence Ground and Aravinda da Silva living near us in Barham. After I ran out of breath he smiled politely, complimented my Spanish and pointed towards a frame at the side of the bar. It's old, he said, but they say it's about your home.

Inside this frame was a set of old 1930s cigarette cards. Each card was a 'Pub of east Kent'. My eye caught the White Hart in Canterbury, the Northern Belle of Margate and the Mariner's of Folkestone. Then sure enough, right at the bottom, was a cigarette card of the pub in my tiny village, Barham. I might have audibly gasped, I don't remember. It hurt, somehow, this frame. It made me feel lonely, adrift and rootless. But it also made me feel, in some way, secure. I knew what I was looking at. I knew exactly what it was. It was a communication that was utterly clear.

The person who had brought this frame to Lima, the bat and trap set, the dart board – they knew what they were doing. They were bringing a slice of east Kent with them to share with Lima. They probably knew that anyone who discovered this pub who knows Kent would feel the way I did. But they probably hoped that the people who don't know east Kent would be intrigued, beguiled and inspired by their trinkets and bric-a-brac.

This, in a long winded way, is how I feel about our anthology, *Connecting Nothing with Something*. It's our attempt to record the south east coast we know, or have experienced. It's our chance to invite writers to send us their literary cigarette cards, stories and poems that invoke a strong sense of place and culture. It's our job to frame them. It's our job to put them in a book for anyone to read. I hope that the writing from this anthology gets knowing nods from men and maids of Kent, chuckles from the Sussex set. Equally, I hope that those with little knowledge of this strange part of the world, will gain some understanding of it through our fictions. I've certainly gained more understanding of my home from editing this collection.

Though short, this anthology is, to me, a great representation of what the south coast offers. It is weighed heavily at each end by the twin tourist towns of Hastings and Margate, with a surreal filling of writing about the places in between these famous small giants. The writing is in turn sharp witted, drunk, melancholic, jealous, happy, isolated and communal. It smells like salt water and hops, late night kebabs and early morning walks on the cliffs. It finds humour in dark places and drama in the small things. It's forever looking somewhere else, yet when it looks away its only ever really looking for itself.

Both Gary and I are aware that nostalgia just ain't what it used to be. The difficulty with putting together a collection about somewhere you grew up and have known for all your years is avoiding a backwards look with a longing gaze. With our selections for *Connecting Nothing with Something*, we've tried to create a perspective that looks straight forward and maybe a little sideways. We've selected writers who are still living in Sussex and Kent, writers who frequently visit and writers who are exiled in places like London. This mix is important, it reflects the nature of the south east coast – a mongrel place of comers and goers, stayers and naysayers. I self-exiled a long time ago but the south east coast of England will always have a hold over me.

When I return to Kent these days, I sometimes long to stay. Maybe this book is my attempt at leaving some permanent part of myself there, within its pages.

Scott Brown presents an exhibition of reassigned memories, detailing Broadstairs, Deal and Folkestone. Look closely and you can come home.

Chimène Suleyman is our introduction to Margate, a drifting narrator out of place and out of season; Iain Aitch explains what would have happened to TS Eliot had he met a bunch of skins in 80s Margate; Gary Budden dives into a Margate of gleaming art and hidden fascism; Daniel Cockrill, Mark Beechill, Rebeccas Dawkins and Katrina Naomi all offer up different poetic interpretations of the town.

Kit Caless takes you on a whirlwind tour of East Kent past and present; fishermen in Deal speak through the medium of Colin Priest. James Arthur Jones offers up ghosts in the port of Dover while the dead have been seen alive by Owen Booth on Romney Marsh.

Reach Hastings and Salena Godden will act as your guide (in 1987); Aziza Abdullah fends off corridor assassins by the sea; Christian Watson feels the stasis of the coast while riots tear apart London. Adrian Self finds traces of Werner Herzog and false Native Americans, and Madeleine McDonald roots through the boxed-up jumble of her life on Hastings prom.

And in Newhaven, Rowena Macdonald shows what happens when the French, so close yet so far, finally appear.

Photograph: Laura Bell

On Margate Sands / I can connect /
nothing with nothing

- TS Eliot

Connecting Nothing
With Something

A Coastal Anthology

I

Headlands

Between the Headlands

An Exhibition of Reassigned Memories

Scott Brown

The exhibition of art featuring locations on south-east England's coastline, *Between the Headlands*, has been on tour for many years now, with recent shows in Dorset, Oxfordshire, London and Paris. The following notes describe just four exhibits, although there are many more available for display; however, it's unusual for more than one item to be on show at any one time.

Shornemead Fort

Polaroid photographs, black & white, x8;
Super 8, colour, 4.13 mins; 2007

I've entered the grainy worlds of voyeurism and espionage.

These eight photographs, mounted in vintage dossiers, offer suggestive glimpses of crumbling masonry and twisted metal: collapsed doorways, blackened bunkers, rusty gun mounts. It feels like under-the-counter heritage porn: a virgin site, illicit. And there's more: Super 8. The Polaroids are evocative enough, but if any medium can be accused of saturating all that it records with a bloated and almost perverse sense of memory, it's cine-film. The muted moving images, fragmented and fragile, deftly impersonate the mind's disjointed quiet, masquerading so close to the idea of remembered truths that they might be accused of theft. This four-minute film of Shornemead Fort, one-time muscle-bound guardian of London, certainly looks that way: stolen. Even the colour has been liberated.

In these images, this bleary-looking, near-forgotten ruin on a lonely plot of Thames estuary marshland, haunt of local children, dog-walkers and few others, appears vulnerable, exposed. The photos coolly highlight particular details; they're precise, whereas the film footage shifts around excitedly, mapping out a plan. It's twitchy. Why? And why too, within this nervously surgical account, are there moments of expansive clarity and calm? One photo has been drowned in a distant, watery view; for a brief moment the film lingers elsewhere too, to shoot a flock of birds in flight. And so, this footage purposely captures another sense of place about the broken bastions: a quintessentially serene one.

Destined for the wrong hands, this reconnaissance locates the prospector's gold. The clues are all there: the dilapidated fort, the quasi-wild locale. Here's an opportunity to impose some false idol upon our collective ante-memory; to make a playground of the past for the amusement of us present. In fact, it may already be too late. The very existence of these images suggests that this process is now long under-way. After all, there is no commodity in things left truthfully abandoned. But value? Yes.

Broadstairs

Oil on canvas; 2010

The almost translucent white flesh, flecked here and there with vermilion, is completely unmistakable; not even the cheap oblong poly-tray or that slapdash blob of mayo can undermine such perfection: this looks divine, it's absolutely lobster. And champagne? No, Babycham! I've not seen that impish little bug-eyed deer for a while, but here he is and I remember him well. A triumph then, I suppose its having achieved such longevity.

Ah . . . shellfish and fizz, on the beach: an afternoon treat on a lazy summer's day, perhaps; lovers, maybe, down from London on the train, gazing out to sea with their modestly decadent fare - not that I can see them or the sea though. It's been better left imagined, calmly lapping at their feet, each wavelet gently wafting its salty perfume along the sand. Left to my own devices, I can picture the little seafood kiosk too, up on the harbour wall; the run-down mini-mart where the booze was bought, next to the amusements arcade. It's all in there.

The diners have probably been waiting their whole lives to arrive at this moment, as the idea for this very meal was surely seeded long ago, back in the 80s when they were both kids. But does that make it merely a faddish indulgence, along with their appreciation of the down-at-heel seaside town? No, this image suggests something altogether more complex: childhood fantasies, once abandoned in adulthood, can be resurrected and made real. It's a heartfelt impression, not a trendy one, which memorialises the seaside as a place where some of our most-loved memories are not only born, but may be reborn, too.

But then again, perhaps I've gone too far.

Maybe it's just lobster and perry on the beach after all, a perennial pleasure that needs no further explanation. Simply that.

Deal

Pencil on paper, x2; 2011

I've seen this before, just a few minutes ago, in the other room. But it's slightly different now, I'm looking at their backs: the viewpoint has switched. In fact, now that I think about it a little more carefully, I realise that the picture's viewpoint hasn't switched at all, so much as mine has. These two sketches are of the same event, mounted back-to-back on either side of the same wall. It's the full 360.

I can see up the beach, and I can see down the beach. The sea is on the right, the sea is on the left. The parked-cars swap sides similarly, the little sea-front cottages too. And in the middle of it all is a small gathering of people.

Back in the other room, I'd noted their slightly battle-worn faces. A hard night previous, I thought, nothing worse than that, but the pencil lines had picked it out perfectly: a wayward clump of hair, a sagging cheek, down-turned corners of lips, dis-poised clothing. I could nearly smell the mature old scotch on their young adult breaths. Just looking at them made me feel a little empathetically rough, and so I wondered: if they could see me, how would I look to them? Would they have regarded me with the same distasteful manner with which they were eyeing the interlopers pictured: a well turned out gentleman and his dog, brisk and bright as the morning air, standing over the party? All eyes were on him and the hound, including mine, but until now I could only see the duo's backs.

Smug. That's his face anyway, the dog's is more disdainful. They might be a pair of well-heeled politicians out to make a Sunday sermon, reminding the now ruinously overindulged of their ultimate inferiority; here to chase these young out-of-towners straight back out of town, where they and their misplaced values belong. What I'm witnessing here is the pre-emptive chit-chat about polarised newspaper allegiances, organic vegetable deliveries and cultural diversity: a passive rouse to mockery and scorn; one-upmanship disguised as discussion.

That would be one reading anyway, one you might expect of a cartoon; satire. And yet, there isn't really that much hostility in these drawings, nor apathy. The heart of these pictures seems to lie elsewhere.

Perhaps these two sketches aren't designed to work as prelude and revelation. For a start, that would be better suited to a linear presentation. Instead, these drawings have been positioned with a kind of independent ambiguity that serves to dispel the tempers of their inhabitants. They're expansive, not scripted. And we, the viewers, have the privilege of seeing this story not just from two sides, but also from afar.

This changes things somewhat, and I realise that the real subject of these sketches might not be the people pictured, but all the lovingly drawn pebbles. There are thousands of them, stretching endlessly along the beach, and apart from a few being displaced by this momentary gathering, the rest remain utterly unaffected by the whim of any person. So used to the sea and its tides, I suppose theirs is a longer and larger view.

Folkestone

Colour photograph; 1997

I can't decide whether the very ordinariness of this scene is unsettling or reassuring: it's a kitchen, decked-out in a now dated but once desirable style. It looks a too new and too old at the same time. A young man, a hooded youth, stands over the sink. I can't see his face. On the floor is a bucket of water with a bottle standing upright in it. Burnt foil makes for a holey bottle top: a gravity bong. The young man has been smoking dope in his parents' kitchen – in their absence, I presume; there's little sign of the folks, except for several empty wine bottles (I doubt they're his).

So this is a snapshot of something quite ordinary after all: the point of disjuncture between parents and their offspring. They're probably a little too adult to really understand or notice, and he's a little too young to know better or care. Lives begin to be lived within the shadows of other lives, surreptitiously: something quite unsettling.

I wonder, where is this kitchen into which I now intrude, this private moment of the absent and unaware family? I know a likely place: a gated community; a self-set trap where the disenchanted resolve to keep-safe, and fail; a place of retreat that by nature defines everything outside to it as hostile. But here, in this lair, in this photograph, is the real source of fear: not the drugs but the no-longer-knowing. The lack of sight.

And yet, we see it.

The designer home has become an asylum by design.

People head to the coast from elsewhere because it's always been a place of sanctuary to them. Day-trippers build castles in the sand; long-stayers lodge in gated communities – they all occupy a fantasy of escape. Beyond such sandy walls not much remains to be well seen, nor much of that which lives within them either, for there is no difference anymore.

The truth was abandoned when they seeded their idea for a fantastic new kitchen by the sea.

But those walls are made of sand, after all, and may be washed away. In their place, where this home was once designed, perhaps another might be found; the family might return once they realise where they are, open the gate, and let it in.

And so there is something reassuring here too. The photo seems to tell us that all is not lost when it might appear so; that when what ought to seem new begins to appear old, you're probably not living in the present. But take a closer look, and you can come home.

II

Margate

They Told the Story From the Lighthouse

Chimène Suleyman

I found Margate watching the sea. I walked the streets thinking they had left it sometime in the `70s, like an old street sign hanging pleadingly over shut cafes. It was an old stand-up comedian who had been successful, lived a rock and roll lifestyle, pissed away his money on hookers and gambling, become an alcoholic, and performed the same routine from `79 in the backs of pubs to old men who all wished they could disappear. It was a wonderful place. My bag was small, not enough clothes for the time there, and a playlist of Stevie Nicks in my ears that soundtracked the walk up the seafront. Out of place Fleetwood Mac posters, too small for the cases they were in, too old to be hanging along the railings. The B&Bs shouldered each other, grey cream grey again. A pretty town, full of fish and chip shops that didn't open and Mayfair packets chased down the road by wind. Spring hadn't come which was fair enough, given that the fat woman with the red dyed hair was stood outside Dreamland in a red vest top, shrugging off the grey sky.

The pub served whisky and cokes that I took my time with,

watched one eye on the football score on the screen across from my head. It felt like a holiday. No real worry for my things, which I left across my seat when I stood out front of the pub smoking, listening to people who knew each other talk. When the pub shut, drunker than I wanted to be, I walked towards the seafront to the line of B&Bs that stood mostly empty. I rang the doorbell and the Lebanese man turned the key on the other side of the glass door opening it. Just him and his wife, and a small child that smelt of shit who turned circles in what should have been their living room. A brown desk and an old computer in the corner as their reception area.

– You waiting for somebody?

– No. I tell him.

– You shouldn't wait for anyone, he says, – no one is worth it.

– No, I say, – it's just me.

– No dirty weekend? he says.

– No.

– That's ok, he says, – it's ok to be here alone, he says, – it's ok.

I paid, took my keys and followed him up to the second floor where the clean double bed was all I wanted, and the shower pissed over the toilet.

I slept well, drunkenness mixed with little sound outside. I woke when the Lebanese man banged on my door at seven in the morning to say his wife had made coffee. I don't know why I was there. A cut-off, a place that had no relevance to my life.

Somewhere I could take the rubbish that was in my head, and dump it, under the nailed-up 'To Let' boards and the old Lido sign that I had more in common with than anything at home; stood on a wall watching over something that didn't exist anymore.

I spent the rest of the morning in the station cafe, avoiding rain. By lunchtime I was in a small ale pub, sat with a fire, ate animals

Illustration: Jay Bernard

in pies, drank, a full day like this. It filled later. The long table beside, each seat taken, where men and women became drunk, and lifted instruments from their cases. They played, sat in their seats around the pub, no fuss for a stage or to be closer to each other or practice and rehearse. They just played, violin, bagpipes the accordion. Braces pulled tight over shoulders, trilby on head.

– Play Irish they said, gypsy, E minor, and the tattoos flashed on arms across the room as they danced through us, the piss goers.

– We're in tune with ourselves, the girl with the big glasses and the round face said, and they tapped hands against chairs.

– Feet makes its own music, this from another person.

Miles from home, them locals, and the music never stopped playing, – A lot happens in a year, a year. And the old guy with the short white beard rolled a cigarette, – in a year, or two, a lot happens in a year, with it's own soundtrack, a lot happens.

I walked the seafront like I fucking got it. Took useless photos of the sea without a flash so it didn't show up. With a bit of moon and flashing colours that kept changing, somewhere around the lighthouse, I fucking got it. I took photo after photo, zigzagged lights on the camera, recorded everything including a pink scribble of light far down on the seafront. They were words, lit up in nighttime, written in neon pink lights and raised out from the dark. Hanging on the front of the white building set back between sea and sky. And I fucking got it. Raced the sea to see it better, chased the lit up neon text further down the seafront, cheered to being away, couldn't feel the season as though I had skipped continents instead of an hour and a half away by train.

I grinned at the sky, thought I had answered all my own questions, thought I had dumped it, and him and you, between ripped posters of dead funfairs and Lido signs. I sang lines from songs, remembered everything with the camera, snapped every bit of black around me as if I couldn't miss a thing. I felt like I had found common ground, seen things in a place that had been more honest with me than home had been. I thought I was free of it all, changed from it all, thanked the sea for its reliability and I walked the seafront, drawn by the brightly lit words further down in pink lights. I stepped out in front of Droid House, the text lit with a pink bulb throughout the night hung from it, white columns, clock at the top. The only bright light on the otherwise dark Golden Mile coming from neon words written across it and I looked up, drunk, released, to read it.

I never stopped loving you.

It says. In brightly lit letters above my head. Always in brightly lit letters above my head. I walked up the hill, a straight walk. The B&B with its lights off, and I sat on the wall and smoked a cigarette.

– Have you got a light? and I handed it to the drunk man, loose clothes, bruises on his face.

– Waiting for something?

– No. And he climbs the stairs at the front of the house, next door to the B&B, the basement of the house dipped far below street level.

He's trying to tell me his name when he falls 20 feet on his head. Fuck. I think. I've just watched a man die. It doesn't matter that he stays alive. Because in my mind he fell to his death, so nothing changes those few seconds. The ambulance people say,

– We think you saved his life. And I don't care.

As I light cigarette off cigarette off cigarette and think he'll do it again soon, and tonight hasn't changed a thing.

The sea looked nice.

You Wantsum?

Iain Aitch

The Isle of Thanet sticks out from mainland Britain like a fist. This makes Margate the country's knuckles, repelling the North Sea, with a tattoo that says 'WANT SUM?' blotted across the tight flesh. The North Sea is the enemy here, as it is the only thing that could possibly be harder than the locals. The only thing that keeps coming back for more. It won't be told.

Historically, most challengers barely make it from the station, never mind past the arcades or that cliff-top shelter where TS Eliot could connect nothing with nothing. If he were here in the 1980s of my youth then someone would have connected a fist with his jaw.

Similarly, the Romans would have stayed in Broadstairs, sipping a latte and enjoying an ironic rum 'n' raisin ice cream. They'd set up camp outside Ramsgate. Do some plumbing work down in Dover. Send the money back home to the wife and kids.

Margate was at its lowest ebb when I was a teenager. The tourists had gone, dole-on-sea was kicking in and the police were on riot watch. The local skinheads drew an invisible border line across the green by the clock tower. Even Mary Portas would have been given the nod to steer clear of the High Street. Margate was a sinking ship, but we were still repelling all boarders.

Back then, Margate was too tough for art. And regeneration was still something that happened on Dr. Who.

If you wanted to see a performance piece then you had to go and witness someone being ejected from the Benjamin Beale public house via a closed window. If primitive line drawings were your thing, then you would take a photo along to the tattooist who operated from beneath the Brutalist tower block on the sea front and he would give it a go.

It helped if your picture was of a dinosaur or a seagull, as all his work looked like one or the other. He was good with names and the initials of football clubs, though, paying particular attention when inking these on the breasts of teenage girls. THFC. Tracey. WHUFC. Joseph. ACAB. LOVE. HATE.

Sticks and stones may break your bones, but words last forever. Even the North Sea can't wash them away and the salty wind that can shred your lips in minutes just draws the ink ever deeper.

If real paintings or sculpture were your thing, you could just skip past the NF stickers on the library doors and enter the gallery above the issuing desk. But the joke was on us. The real art was above the door to the library, in the shape of Michael Craig-Martin's neon book with its graceful, slow turning pages.

A version of this work now sits behind the reception desk at the Turner Contemporary gallery, reminding locals of long waits for buses, overdue book fines and being up before the Juvenile Court. The library shared an entrance with the courts, though few took the opportunity to mix a trial for GBH with perusing the watercolours.

Turner Contemporary marked the turning of a corner for

Margate when it opened in 2011, after a ten-year wait for it to materialise at the spot where the old enemy, the North Sea, is at its most fearsome. Although, Margate had already started to embrace the arts before that. The tipping point being in September 2006, when Laurie Anderson was spotted having an al fresco cuppa just before locals set fire to an Antony Gormley sculpture.

I should point out that this arty conflagration was part of an Artangel film project. Margate likes to come out and watch a fire, but they are usually ones set by property developers or gangsters, keen to speed up the planning process. Regeneration by jerry can.

Perhaps more importantly, this was the day that arty types crossed the invisible line, parading their jaunty hats and jauntier hairstyles along the prom, prom, prom without so much as a bloody nose. Soon they were arriving on the high-speed train, thousands of them. Pouring from the station like a sandy version of Rourke's Drift. Too many for even the last few remaining local skins to repel.

Catch the last fast train back to St Pancras after a private view now and you could hear accents honed at public schools. Art dealers. Agents. Speculators. All aboard The Art Wanker Express.

Only the locals know it is called that. Just like they know that the Turner Contemporary is really called the Turner Centre, Tracey Emin is called Tracey Emins and that you should always ignore the pedestrian crossing that interrupts the High Street. Pedestrians have right of way. Just plough across. Cars can't hold back the North Sea. We can.

The winds from the ice age batter you hardest at the top of the Scenic Railway, but that momentary glimpse of death as you fall from the first drop makes you feel so alive. The Russians put a man into orbit, but we have been experiencing zero gravity in

Margate since 1920. We have seen the future. We have always seen the future.

This time the future is art, cupcakes, retro shops (somewhat ironically) and a growing middle-class. Like all other futures, this will crash and burn one day. But, for now, the town is changing to the beat of Sonic Youth, playing cards in the spokes of fixed wheel bikes and pre-natal classes.

Released from the rabbit hutches of Hackney, arty couples find space to breed in the six-bedroom former boarding houses that sit haughtily side-on to the crashing waves. Phil and Kirsty beam with pride. These are the immigrants that the locals don't complain about, at least not too much. DFLs. Down From London. You can't paint swastikas to scare them off. Anyway, they have money and they know how to make their own pasta.

This meeting of old and new is not always the most comfortable. The road from the seafront pubs to the new gallery and its café may as well be a pit of snakes for some born and bred locals. And the new arrivals despair when seeing a shirtless local who does not have a beard and who is drinking supermarket lager un-ironically.

But the old skinhead pubs now offer fish and chips with a mushy pea smear and the slightly-too-old-to-be-hipsters find themselves accidentally mixing with the down-at-heel who use charity shops for real rather than for dress up. This is not a permanent impasse. Margate was modernist before the mods arrived. We had space-age architecture before anyone had coined the phrase. Margate adapts, Margate copies the pattern and sells it on the market at the weekend. Push, push, push, push.

You don't have to be born with the words running through your bones like sweet, sticky seaside rock, it just seeps in. You can dip your toe in the sea anywhere in the world and you are back home again. Everywhere in the world touches Margate and every drop of salt water has visited at least once. The place has more soul than the sum of every soul weekender there has ever been.

Dance on the sand like no one is watching and keep an eye on the North Sea for the rest of us.

Photograph: Laura Bell

Margate is . . .

Daniel Cockrill

a long shadow
a broken window
a torn poster
a tongue-tied roller coaster

an original Turner
a single mother
a window seat that's taken
a blind Nelson

a down season grotto
a drained lido
a jellied eel
an empty shell

a tidal town
a fragile frown
things I'll never understand
a Dreamland.

The Exhibition

Gary Budden

The City

Sirens and shrieks punctured the gloom. Somewhere out there, glass shattered. I listened to the night and packed my bag, a few changes of clothes, toothpaste and soap, a tongue-in-cheek book on punk rock and genre theory. I phoned my father. I told him when I would be arriving the following morning. He agreed to pick me up from the station. We would drive the rest of the way. I slept fitfully, alone, beset by muggy dreams of ancient coastlines, Victorian bathers in porno poses, an immediate family who never visited.

Morning came, weak summer light rousing me. I got ready fast, grabbed my pre-packed bag and headed out to the nearest tube. I stared at commuters doing their daily grind. Their faces were inscrutable, locked down. I listened to loud, angry hardcore to block out The City.

I arrived at the transport hub, sweating slightly. I bought an overpriced greasy pasty and bit in too early. The filling burned my tongue. I gulped down coffee. Notice boards reconfigured and informed me of my imminent departure. I boarded the train, to take me out of The City, to The Exhibition.

The Train

The Train was largely empty. I read my book, munched my pasty and drained my coffee. I was beginning to feel human again, the hangover slowly dissipating.

The City ebbed away and my home county began, the land flattening out, green overtaking concrete and the suburban conurbations fading into farmland. I gazed at grazing cows. I read about a black fox sighting in a discarded *Daily Mail*. A sign of ill-omen in British folklore. A photo of its dead and battered body, snuffed out by traffic, stood as the article's centrepiece.

An hour and twenty minutes dragged by, until my rendezvous with my father at Herne Bay station. I stepped out onto the platform, we hugged, said how good it was to see each other. I was surprised to discover that I meant what I said.

The Drive

This was a rare trip out of The City back to the homelands. My father was pleased I was there. I hadn't seen him in six months. We share many similar interests. We chatted every few weeks over the phone about how the Tories were gutting the country, of how West Ham were doing, what interesting documentaries we'd been watching on BBC4. I missed him. I'd nod and smile as he repeated that things now were the same as – no, worse – than the early 1980s when I was born. He had said this many times before, as if repetition made his point stronger. He repeated himself, and what he said was true. When we met in the flesh, conversation became more difficult, divergent cross purposes and overlapping sentences, endless tautologies and no substance. I hoped The Exhibition would burst the dam. On the phone, describing The Exhibition, he was more enthusiastic that I had heard him in years.

It was a short drive to Margate, my father talking of local events and family members who I never saw and rarely thought about. BBC Kent mumbled softly on the stereo about local traffic issues, the effect of the Crossrail, an upcoming Oyster Festival on a more fashionable stretch of the coast, and The Exhibition. Local pundits discussed how this would benefit the area. The word 'bohemian' was used. The coast was hidden for most of the short drive. I daydreamed of Kentish selkies, mermaids and sirens.

We passed a giant structure named, Thanet Earth. The UK's largest, most high-tech greenhouse complex, according to my father. The name made me smile.

Faint drizzle speckled the windows as we raced up the Thanet Way, passed St Nicholas-at-Wade roundabout and onto the Canterbury Road through Birchington. The houses we passed were slathered in Union Jacks, bunting hanging like rotten fruit off the houses, beads of moisture adhering to the cheap plastic nationalism. The royals had been up to something of late that seemed to make people happy. I struggled to remember. The coast made me an amnesiac and fretful.

'Lot of Union Jacks,' said my father.

The next town along the route, Westgate, was much the same. Here, even a few St. George's crosses sat flapping in the breeze. Everywhere, the bunting.

Finally, we reached the town, the sweep of the coastline stretching away in front of us in a majestic curve, the harbour visible with a few boats bobbing on the waves. The Gallery, our destination, stood alone and metallic in the distance. To our right, a towering block of flats stood guard over a defunct and boarded up Dreamland. A temporary black-and-yellow sign stuck to a lamp-post pointed the curious in the direction of the 'Margate Museum of Monstrosities'.

We parked up in sight of the beach, paid the modest fare, and headed into The Old Town. That was the quickest route, my father said, unless you wanted to cut through Primark. I wrinkled my nose at the thought.

The Old Town

We entered The Old Town.

A public information point, rendered in tasteful black and gold and carrying Margate's coat-of-arms, proudly announced:

1736 – ENGLAND'S EARLIEST SEASIDE RESORT – 1736

I dutifully took a photograph on my iPhone for my records. I scribbled the info in my notebook. My father had already passed the sign.

Letters advertising the *Thanet Times* faded on the brickwork, reminiscing about better days. Red and yellow-beaked herring gulls were flitting anxiously in the rooftops. Coastal gulls, I knew, were in decline, almost red list now according to the RSPB. They were adapting too well to our cities, our landfill sites and shitheaps. 'Seagull' was now a misnomer.

However redundant they were, this was their patch. They screeched incessantly and pirouetted above the sluggish rooftops, their shit covering the peeling messages that informed of *Thanet's Best Sport* and *The Weekend's Best News*. I stared up at the sky as my father surged ahead, enthusiastic in the faint drizzle, the grey and pervasive damp. It was reassuring English seaside weather. I wrapped it around myself, comforted by the drizzly panacea. I couldn't recall this place ever being sunny, being warm. The town, like the host-country, didn't exist without the wet, the dull and patient rain. One of the gulls launched off a terracotta chimney with an ear splitting cry, heading in the direction of the murky sea. We, however, were heading in the direction of The Exhibition. An old woman, her outfit a rainbow of pastel shades, shuffled by, her gaze directed with bored curiosity toward me. I felt too tall in places like this. As I looked away, ashamed, I noticed a bunch of discarded yellow carnations, lying in a dustbin.

England slumbered in the rain, a calming pitter-patter that kept us in dreamtime. The sun ruined this and closed down the gateways. I liked the rain. In the past it was always raining.

'Come on!' shouted my father, not unkindly, now a hundred feet away.

Last week he had returned from a trip to Lindisfarne. I feared he was going to expand on his tales of bar-tailed godwits and pintail in the pub, after The Exhibition. 'Lindisfarne', he'd informed me, 'was the location used for Roman Polanski's *Cul de Sac*.' He was a closet cineaste. 'Polanski is a nonce', I had retorted, and was met with disapproving silence.

All Margate had to offer, he said, was an adaptation of Graham Greene's Last Orders. It starred Ray Winstone and Michael Cain. He was wrong.

'What about Pawlikowski's *Last Resort*?' I asked. He snorted. I don't think he'd watched it, even after my recommendations.

That film hadn't been received well by the town's denizens, a decade ago now, viewed more favourably in the liberal broadsheets. 'Poor Margate,' they crooned, then talked about famous artists and the vanishing working class. In that film, the town was dubbed 'Whitehaven', but we all knew the truth. Dirty asylum seekers, depression hanging like mist in the sea air, Eastern European women forced into pornography, vodka and cheap fags, Dreamland and Paddy Considine. A typical British exercise in misery.

My foot snagged on some greasy chip wrappers left as appeasement to the gulls. I shook it off, and followed my father. I could feel the old woman's gaze boring into my back.

Running after him, I noticed a glut of small boutique stores, selling hand crafted jewellery, local art, hand woven objects of no practical use. The shops looked empty.

I thought of Helena.

The Dreamtime

Helena, a friend with artistic tendencies made in my mid-twenties in The City, told me that this place – fucking Margate – was the place of her birth. In a city where everyone I met was Polish, Finnish, Canadian or Colombian, this was unbearably exotic. In the years before we had met, I would lie in the siren-shredded multicoloured night, trapped in squalid bedsits, thinking erotic thoughts about mythical women from the Home Counties, scanty clad beauties from the Garden of England, with thick estuary accents in states of incandescent arousal. I would stare at the Turkish girls standing outside their cafes on summer days, Bangladeshi sylphs on Brick Lane and feel ashamed that I didn't want them.

Helena had a tattoo on her back that resembled Giger's more overtly sexual work, and dyed cobalt-blue hair. A malachite necklace always hung low around her neck. She was a fan of hardcore punk, epic crust and post-metal. I suggested to her that it was a male dominated subculture. What did she see in it?

'Sometimes' she answered, 'I hate my interests.'

I replied, 'I wish I was more connected to my family's working class roots. I'm adrift.'

'You know we remember back at least three generations, through the oral histories passed down through our parents, grand-parents, the retold stories of the dead, of our ancestors.'

She grinned as she said this.

'I can't outwit or outrun my landscape,' I answered, and started humming Chas and Dave's 'Margate'.

'You can keep the Costa Brava and all that palava, going no farther, me I'd rather have me a day down Margate with all me family.'

'We are the landscape,' she slurred, drunk.

'Who?' I asked, but Helena never replied.

We would talk of that seaside town, neither of us sure if it still existed, of Dreamland and Albion's dreamtime, our myths of an arboreal past, gritty sand, sad childhood memories of Kent and the early 1990s, antediluvian visions of the town before the floods of 1949. We shared history here, had both seen The Levellers play at the Winter Gardens, back in '98. She'd tell me about her favourite sea monsters, inform me of Margate, USA, near Atlantic City and I would nod without understanding.

One summer we had travelled through the old Cinque Ports, climbed down their Limbs kicking our feet through salt spray, sand and shingle. We stood firm and picnicked on the silted land that was once the Wantsum Channel. We searched in vain for memento moris of an absent sea. We clambered over Roman ruins, National Heritage audio-tours blocking out the sound of the gulls, ate sandwiches in Sandwich with the Pfizer chemical plant austere in the background. We stayed at my mother's, on the coast, where we drank tea, ate more sandwiches and exchanged pleasantries. Since The Exhibition, much has changed.

When in The City, Helena and I would sit on curb-sides outside of punk shows with the rest of the voluntary outcast, swigging Special Brew from stolen cans. I would begin singing that Bad Manners classic to scowling or embarrassed passersby. Buster Bloodvessel, I would mention as I did every time this happened, ran Fatty Towers in Margate. It closed back in '98.

'I know,' Helena said, 'you've told me that before. A place for fat cunts.'

I was a broken Trojan ska seven-inch.

We wondered whether the National Front, holding rallies there in the early two thousands, were ska fans, skinheads, or just racists with no sub-cultural leanings.

The Skinheads

Margate had its very own skinhead shop. The question of how it turned a profit consumed me. The rents, I observed as I wandered through The Old Town with my father, were very low. Many shop fronts were boarded up, nestling next to blooming gastropubs with embarrassed architecture. We entered, Desmond Dekker's 'Israelites' leaking out of the stereo as a huge bald man in a 2-Tone t-shirt nodded silently along in assent. I was not a skinhead, but the Harringtons appealed. I had read Richard Allen with some interest, owned Doc Martens, and listened to The Oppressed and other anti-fascist Oi! I had the Trojan Skinhead Reggae Collection saved on my Spotify playlist.

Posters of The Specials, The Beat and Madness, adorned the walls. A vinyl reissue of The Last Resort's *Skinhead Anthems: A Way of Life* sat on the counter in stark red, white and blue. I was ambivalent toward the colour-scheme.

I had asked the hulk behind the counter if he knew if I could find any of the Allen novels anywhere. I was particularly after *Suedehead*.

'Not much chance, mate' he said amiably. 'Even the reprints go for thirty quid a pop on eBay.'

The adjoining shop catered for the cybergoths and the psytrance crowd. I didn't really know what it was. Dance music and I had a fractious relationship. When pushed I'd would dance with chemical enthusiasm to dubstep and drum 'n' bass. The girl at the desk was an attractive day-glo rainbow, dreadlocks hanging low over her breasts, a faint smile. Did she actually live here? I was too timid to ask.

I thought of Helena, long disappeared now. Where did she go? Surrey, East Lothian or the Gower, perhaps to Whitehaven. I thought of her and the other Kentish-born. I myself was raised, not born, in that county. Birthed onto the tarmac of the North Circular, then shuttled a few years later down to develop by an amnesiac coastline, in a land of salt marshes, rusting arcades, bowling greens and as the years went on, day trippers from The City and coastal olive vendors. I fought it, but this was the place that I still thought of as home. The desire for an indigenous metropolitan status was becoming rotten.

Helena could always sidestep this problem. She was fine with loving The City and the coast equally, both things informed her and her work. She claimed there were no tensions or contradictions within her. The City and coast were simply different areas on her psychic map, it was all one and the same in the British Dreamtime.

'If The City were by the sea' she stated 'then that would be perfection.'

I would roll my eyes at this. In the years after she had left, I had slowly understood. All the places I visited outside of The City becoming one. Scafell Pike, Lindisfarne, Stodmarsh, The Hole of Horcum, backstreets in Manchester, Birmingham's Bullring, the city walls in York, Pegwell Bay, the Thames Barrier, these were all significant parts of my life, hard to pull apart and rank in order of importance.

By the time I had realised all this, Helena had been out of my life for years. I no longer even had an email contact and Facebook searches yielded nothing. It was a rare skill to truly disappear.

The Seafront

My father and I exited the skinhead store, leaving The Old Town, passing a shabby and thronged Primark, ice cream vendors in catatonic states and fungal gastropubs. We found ourselves confronted suddenly with the sea, a roiling grey mass, too cold today for swimmers. The long arcade, a gamut for us to run, was our route to The Exhibition.

It stretched for miles, Victorian lamp posts lurching out of the pavement, young couples arm in arm laughing with each other, a muttering homeless man swigging cider on a promenade bench, the glittering arcades flashing neon and promising more than they could give.

'What is The Exhibition, really, Dad?' I asked.

'You'll see. You'll love it son.' He leaked smoke. I clutched my vinyl copy of *Skinhead Anthems* that I had purchased.

On we marched, toward a shimmering beacon of Art, The Gallery, that housed The Exhibition. It shimmered in peripheral vision, beckoning tourists toward it. Scribbling in my notepad I wrote 'Eloi walking cheerfully to their doom' then immediately scratched it out, trying to think of something more direct and less patronising.

There were ongoing debates whether The Gallery's energies were regenerative or vampiric. I had my plan, my plan to hate it and assume my usual anti-posture. It was expected of me. I had to visit the place to do this convincingly. I was aware of my hypocrisy, my lack of purity, my inability to ignore. I fed The Exhibition and The Gallery with my own pointless discourse and they grew plump and healthy on scorn and disapproval.

Bored herring gulls hung in a sky suspended as we entered the cavernous gate that led into The Exhibition. Strangely uniformed attendants stood watch, fiddling with their mobile phones.

'We're here,' stated my father, bursting with pride and satisfaction that he'd lured me down from the toxic city of his youth, of my adulthood.

Rodin's *The Kiss* welcomed us into the building. To its right, curiously, was the gift shop, situated before The Exhibition.

Small groups of tourists milled around, examining tote bags, flicking through Taschen art books, browsing the selection of postcards on a squeaky spinner. I heard Philadelphia accents, murmurings in Japanese and German. Many, many voices like my own. Women uttering their erotic estuary vowels. My mind flooded with images of tattooed women in Victorian bathing suits, frolicking in the brine while the Industrial Revolution flickered in the background, all set to a skinhead ska soundtrack. I fought to control myself and focused on a badly designed guide to the work of J.M.W. Turner.

Over my shoulder – 'He was from Margate.'

'I know, Dad.' I smiled at my father's repetition, reassured. If pressed, I wouldn't be able to expand on this or name any of the paintings.

My composure regained, we entered The Exhibition.

The Exhibition

To my right was a grainy photo portrait of a young Arthur Rimbaud. I recalled *Sonnet to an Asshole* with a smirk as we shuffled into the main art-hangar.

I stepped inside. The ceiling was miles above, half-tame herring gulls wheeling and screeching, enjoying the warmth. They were modernising, moving with the times in a way that I never could. Gull shit occasionally splattered on the floor, on the exhibits, on us. A fat blob of guano landed on my Last Resort LP.

'Bollocks!' I hissed. My father shot me a look.

'Look,' he said.

Spread out in front of me was a psychic map of Britain. A map of my entire life and everything I ever held dear.

A kraken tentacle, allegedly washed up on Margate's shore in the mid nineteenth century, floated sadly in a tank of preservative fluid a hundred metres high.

A wall, every able bit of space used, displayed an exhaustive record of British counter-culture in the 70s, 80s and 90s.

I was staggered.

'I told you you'd like it,' laughed my father. I was thrilled that he still knew me so well.

The weight of information, the visual barrage, nearly buckled me at the knees.

Kentish accents murmured threateningly in the distance. I could feel a panic attack coming on.

An American woman, shrill with culture, ignored the signs and snapped away on her iPhone camera. None of the attendants bothered to stop her.

Slogans from my past, our past, were everywhere.

CLASS WAR. CHARIOTS OF FIRE!

Charles and Diana peering out of a gaudy Union Jack / Butcher's Apron.

A poster of Duran Duran.

An original poster from the anarchist punk band Conflict. WAR ON THE STREETS it declared.

WHO DO THEY THINK THEY'RE FOOLING? YOU?

An Angelic Upstarts gig poster. Two million voices murmuring and not listening to each other.

The Clash, FREE THE H-BLOCK PRISONERS, Cockney Rejects, grotesque Thatcher caricatures, a promo poster for The Raincoats. Prickles licked up my spine as I looked at an old Skrewdriver badge. Nasty Nazi pamphlets from back in the day, Blood and Honour, Combat 18 totenkopfs, skinhead bootboy violence, boneheads; the rotten side of this fucked country's past. I thought of the behemoth owner of the skinhead emporium, what his politics were, what he did on an average day.

Whoever had curated The Exhibition, had gathered this underground ephemera, really knew their stuff. I felt envy.

My father, smiling, led me to another part of The Exhibition. Pictures of me, my younger brother and sister at various stages in our development. Holding Christmas presents. Smiling in school orchestrated photographs. Standing muddy in a campsite in the Lake District somewhere near the base of Scafell Pike. Birds of prey grasping leather bound arms, at a falconry out in Oxfordshire.

I wish I knew where my brother was, what my sister did with her time. In that moment their absence was palpable. Kent dwellers as they were, they saw my mother and father regularly. I had not seen them since Christmas two years back.

My mother featured in none of these photos, and I struggled to picture her face in my mind's eye. I thought of Helena and I, sipping tea with her in Whitstable on a rainy summer's day before a cycle trip to Reculver.

I excused myself, ran to the toilet passing a painting of Victorian bathers, and vomited. Last night's excess letting me know it hadn't forgotten me. I wiped the bile from my lips, feeling better. I took a piss, washed my hands and face with clean cold water. An old man next to me hacked a blob of phlegm into the urinal.

I returned to The Exhibition.

Another wall. Accounts from old punks and skinheads, portraits of them now in middle-to–pushing-old-age juxtaposed with them caught in the frames of blurry Polaroids as teenagers, as young men and women. Typed up accounts of what it all meant to them clung lichen-like to the walls, these youth trips down to Margate to indulge their marginal cultures in a marginal place. Didn't they realise that they'd been imprisoned, compartmentalised, made a part of a history they never wanted? What did I know. I was a middle-class pretender, a parasite. Maybe they realised, and didn't care, or relished the delayed appreciation. BBC4 were doing their Punk Britannia season soon, docs on John Cooper Clarke and The Adverts. I was looking forward to reminiscing about things I was too young to remember. But Helena . . . Helena had told me that our memories stretched back as far as our ancestors. I hadn't seen her for years and thought of her every day. We were never lovers. I wondered why an artful photo of her, drunk, was attached to the kraken tank. I always made a point of going into exhibitions, plays and movies, blind. I said it made it fresh.

My question was soon answered. The next section of The

Exhibition was devoted entirely to the work of my once-and-future friend, Helena Williams. I read a gushing biographical blurb neatly typeset onto the wall of The Exhibition in a modern, progressive font. The errant prodigal daughter, returned to the 180 degree town of her youth, was the mastermind of The Exhibition, curator, exhibitor, artist, saviour. Everything she was needed to be. I imagined a few broadsheet journalists would disagree, but their opinion meant little these days.

I paused to stop and examine a set of line drawings entitled *Anthropological Study of the Kentish Male, Removed From His Natural Habitat, The City 2005.*

There I was, rendered in charcoal, can of Special Brew clutched in my fist, outside a sketch of a pub in New Cross. She had made me look thinner than I was in our so-called real life, and was thankful for that.

My father rejoined me.

'That's you, son,' he said.

'I know dad, she was my friend'.

'Who was?'

Elsewhere I was treated to *Salt Woman,* a bizarre self-portrait rendered in dyed salt crystals. *Anthropological Study of Kentish Female, Margate Seafront, 1998,* depicted a young woman drunk and alone on a wintry coast. *The Last Resort* was a collage with unsettling fascist and skinhead imagery. *The Kraken of Kent, Ice Cream Ossuary, Memories of Meregate, Giving up the Coast, Cinque or Swim, Re-degeneration* and *The Dreamtime / Ben Bomb Brothers.* A disturbing and inspirational collection. The work of, I realised, a major artist. I felt proud and envious of her, ashamed of my own limited artistic successes.

She'd been prolific in the time since we'd last seen each other.

I had done nothing but drink and lose myself in psychotropics looking for an Albion I knew wasn't there. I fingered the punk-pastiche tattoo on my left arm.

We spent a good hour in Helena's room. I hoped there were prints available. *Anthropological Study of the Kentish Male, Removed From His Natural Habitat, London 2005* would make a good set of postcards. I could send one to my mother.

In the gift shop, taken with The Exhibition as I was, I rushed to buy the accompanying book. It was plump with observation and discourse, printed on heavy paper, full of portent. Reproductions of Helena's work stood in full colour in the middle centrepiece section. The girl behind the till was the same harlequin attendant from the cybergoth shop. She flashed a quicksilver smile, uttered the phrase 'ten pounds' with such sultry Southern English vowels that I became a babbling mess. My father just shook his head. I handed over a crumpled note and scuttled away.

We left The Exhibition, left The Gallery, and headed toward the nearest boozer. Only gastropubs seemed open for business, so we settled in the nearest one with a view over the grey sea and ordered ourselves pints of lager and portions of greasy cod and onion rings. My father started talking of bar tailed godwits. I gulped down alcohol.

The Last Resort

That night I stayed at my father's, eating Bombay aloo, tarka daal and chapattis. We drank cold canned lager. I slept on the sofa. In the morning I boarded a train that sped me back to The City.

On the train, desperately trying to ignore a group of late-teenage girls who sat drinking and planning their daytrip in the metropolis, I recalled the last time I'd seen Helena.

I knew she was leaving. I pretended not to care. We necked Jagermeister, dabbed powders out of a dirty plastic wrap, watched a local punk band who we agreed were shite. One last chance to experience nothing changing.

We talked about working-class parents, how we defined ourselves and the places where we grew up, of how she wanted to pursue her art and realise some of the crazy thoughts she had running through her head. I had always encouraged her. I said to her that I thought the whole punk-skin subculture may have some life in it yet, room for more stories. Who got to put the final full-stop on the narrative? She nodded enthusiastically. She talked of how she wanted to leave The City, do something different, she was never going to focus on her art in this place. She needed salt and shingle.

'Remember the Wantsum Channel?'

I nodded sadly. She was the last woman I'd ever known with that accent.

'I want to go home' she said.

We'd said goodbye as I put her on a crowded night bus. I waved as the bus pulled away. I'd bought a can of super strength cider from the local offie, and walked home through The City.

Celebration my Arse

Mark Beechill

Another weird birthday
Performance art on the beach
Surrounded by morons
Margate's ongoing mission
To polish its own turd

Woken up by cunts at three in the morning
I wander, half dazed
The empty desolate streets
Of another rotting seaside relic

Breakfast in pub
Where everyone else's breakfast
Is a pint
And the most exciting thing to happen
Is the sporadic wail of the fire alarm
That
Like all the other shit in this town
Seems impossible to fix

Visitors

Katrina Naomi

'Visitors' and 'Tunnel of Love' first appeared in The Girl With the Cactus Handshake *(Templar Poetry)*

The windows were open, but they usually knocked at the
                                          back door,
and you'd hear them, not just the toy town tinkle of Mr Whippy
that my friend's mum told him meant he'd run out of lollies and
                                          ice cream,
but the calls from the Corona lorry, *lemonade, lemonade*, though
he had limeade, orangeade, cherryade, Tizer, ginger beer,
                                          sarsaparilla.
The milko had already been but Mr Corona only visited Edinburgh
                                          Walk
on Fridays, took the empties for a penny off, as I thumbed the
                                 bumps on the bottles.
There was the rag-n-bone on a Saturday, in a mesh-sided cart,
and my new dad doubled up winter and summer, delivering coal
                                          and turf.

The fish man called on Fridays too, he didn't need a jingle,
you could smell him all the way from the sea. At Christmas,
it was the Sally Army Band and mum always had the same

request,
sent me out in my Led Zep sweatshirt to ask for 'In the Deep

Mid-winter'.
Once or twice there was a knife sharpener, on a bike, who also did

scissors.
When the Christian Aid collectors came mum said to put a few

tuppences in,
made it feel like ten pence pieces in the red paper wallets. One

year,
the Sally Army brought us a grocery box, covered with silver foil
and inside, a ham, oranges, cake. It made mum cry, even before

they'd played.
The clairvoyant arrived, unannounced. Told mum her future,

wanted no payment..

Tunnel of Love

Katrina Naomi

It looked uncertain.
I tottered in, heels
skittering on the pink plastic.
There were water trails
before the pleasure boat rocked.
My rocker was on board.

I say 'my' he was anyone's,
with his bleached, blond quiff,
curl caressing his left eyebrow,
scar bisecting the right,
so he looked almost symmetrical,
apart from his hands.

His hands were all over me,
before we'd even sat
on the wet, moulded seats.
And I never did. I sat on his lap.
My neat, white pencil skirt,
tight as a condom.

He couldn't pull it up or down.
It wrinkled along my untouched body,
wedged against his heaving drainpipes.
Yet we bobbed, as one,
bashed into the fake grass
and the fibre glass cave, together.

I had so little for him to squeeze,
as we juddered through the darkness.
His hormones masked by Brut,
£1.99 from the precinct,
and that gorgeous roll-up,
which tasted all the better on his tongue.

He called it his 'shag break',
his other recreation,
aside from riding the dodgems,
leaping from one to another
with balletic ease in his narrow jeans,
like a sexy bus conductor.

And he was thin, tight muscles
alert in his black t-shirt,
little more than a boy.
Yet he looked so much older,
cruising the dodgems with his sneer,
chipped tooth and chiselled hair

I knew enough to keep my hands
out of his hair. I kissed him hard,
slid off his lap in the sunshine.
He didn't help me out of the boat,
just lit another cigarette, its tip
sparking the way to the electric cars.

Senescence

Rebecca Dawkins

Vegas lights, those sunny holidays, that endless laughter.
Rickety-rides, piercing screams as pink clouds melted on my
tongue.
Deck chair stripes, gritty sandwiches and breath-snatching water.

Empty windows, sex shops and Primark.
Not too many memories, just
Yellow lines, rain and shame.

Art and culture incarnate in this rock washed up to shore,
Rock-pooling in the high street; little gems unearthed, delight in
each endeavour,
I grew up with you old friend, now it's time to stop the tide.

III

East Kent

Old but Somehow New

Kit Caless

Whitstable

We smoked hash on the slopes while the bands played pub rock. He looked salty and tasted warm when we kissed. I wanted to jump on all the boats and sail them to far away places that we couldn't imagine. But university had pulled me away.

'You'll be back,' he said. And he was right.

Herne Bay

Adam's 16th birthday party just got famous. The police arrived, kicked out all the kids, confiscated alcohol, weed and turned off the music.

Adam overheard someone say on the way out, 'Mate, Adam's party was so good the police had to shut it down!'

Adam smiled; he had called the police. Finally, he was popular.

Margate

I met a Brazilian PhD student at a Sukkot party in Belsize Park.

'You are from Kent?' she said, 'maybe you can answer me this. Why are old things so important in England?'

I told her we are a nostalgic people. She said, 'what does this word 'vintage' mean?'

I said, 'old but somehow new.'

Photograph: Laura Bell

Ramsgate

We push two pence coins through the slots. The coins pile up over the edge. They almost drop this time. One more go, again. You tell me you like me. I say if this fiver falls I'll buy you a Tangle Twister. You shake the machine to help me. The alarm goes off.

We run.

Sandwich

'Why is it called a Cinque Port, when there's no port?'

'It's ex-coastal, like . . . it used to have a coast.'

'How can you have a coast in the past?'

'Silted up didn't it? The sea's two miles away these days.'

'I see. What about Pfizers?'

'They've gone now. Three thousand redundancies.'

'That's pretty stiff.'

'Quite.'

Barham

Chris had heard of this thing called 'guerilla gardening' they did in London. Illegally planting flowers around the city. It sounded daring and romantic. Chris had just read *No Logo* by Naomi Klein. He went out one night and did it. However, nobody noticed in the morning. That's the trouble with living in a village.

Deal

'Let's go Tides!' I shout, suddenly inspired.

'What's Tides?' she asks.

'A swimming pool we used to go to in Deal, they got this massive wave machine and huge flumes. It's amazing. You'll love it!'

Half an hour later and the pool's tiny, the waves miniscule, the disappointment large. I slide on the crocodile sheepishly.

Dover

Brendan shakes chips onto the child's school lunch plate.

'I got in a fight last night,' he says, 'down the Eight Bells.'

The child stares at him.

'Looks at these knuckles sunshine . . . '

The child's eyes widen.

'He interrupted me on the fruity. I was just about to get the jackpot repeater. So I lamped him.'

Canterbury

They stumbled into Northgate `Spoons.

'Man up boys,' shouted the best man, 'let's get the beers in.'

The lads puffed out their chests and cheered. The stag was quiet. What he really wanted to do was hike up a mountain and have a meal in a country pub. But no one had listened to him.

St Margaret's Bay

I was in the rock pools, chasing crabs with my fingers when Rachel found a fully formed jaw in the caves. The teeth had gold fillings. Sally said we should throw it back in the sea. We didn't tell Mum. In the car, Rachel whispered, 'What if there was a body too?' and Sally cried.

Folkestone

They came for the Folkestone Triennial. Walked through the town, saw the mermaid, the rusty horse of nails, Wallinger's stones. Took the Lea's Lift. Walked the sculpted sea path. Drank in the Mariners. Had tea at The Grand. Then they took the HS1 train back to London and didn't return for three more years.

Hythe

Sarah sloshes vinegar all over her chips. Her fingers already blackened by the newspaper ink. 'These are the best chips!' she declares to the ducks on the canal. They quack in agreement and gather at her feet. A handsome man rows past. She throws a chip at him. It smacks him right on the nose.

Lydd

Mike drives down the Romney Road. Ed is on the phone to the car in front. Bad Company's 'Son of Nitrous' reaches the drop. The six by nines rumble heavy bass. Chris flails limbs in the passenger seat. *Who holds a rave in a fucking airport?* Mike thinks to himself. Then come the flashing lights.

Dungeness

Rob takes Satu to Dungeness.

'You won't believe what it looks like.'

Rob is besotted with the dystopian vision of a post-apocalyptic Kent. He dreams of Kent's domineering heritage destroyed, withered by nuclear fall out and ravaged by revolution. When they reach the headland, Satu says, 'What's the big deal? It looks just like Finland.'

Greetings from DEAL

Three Men Talking About the Weather

Colin Priest

M   Did you see the bench outside the castle - snapped sharp
Booted.

R   The wood looks . . .

L   Rotten,
Council needs to know about that,
Will cause an injury.

M   Compensation smugglers.

R   It was probably you waiting for Walrus to come in, you
fat bast'rd.

L   Good catch then?

M   Doubt it – pier tomb-stoners keepin' them away,
        Can't blame 'em – hottest day in the year,
        Wardens were busy with the Regatta
        A teddy bears picnic, a music concert and an airstream
        caravan.

M   Lets hope no one breaks their neck before summer is
        over.

L   Did you hear about Stumpy?
        Eatin' the lugworm left-overs.

R   No left foot – just a limb,
        Dead.
        Found under the newly timbered pier . . .
        Lines are turning out a good catch though
        Must be the tide.

M   P&O keepin' the gulls content;
        Circling scavengers.

L   Magic that.
        Fish and Chips on Middle Street won an award . . .

M   Second best fish supper in the country.
        Battered Rig.

L   Stationers on High Street closed at the start of the year.

R   Cleared out in a week and then left empty.

L   And the music shop opposite the town hall.

M   Took ages to paint that place white.
       Change.
       Pah.
       Teashops and decorating help . . .

L   Vintage we called new.
       Time-bombed.

R   Picked up a book on the coast in Oxfam last week'nd,
       Beside the seaside, a celebration of the beach
       Load of rocks.

L   Nostalgia?

M   Stones last longer than stories.

R   Those old bench plaques,
          Do they get fixed to new benches?

L   Beside the seaside;

M   Salted souls watching the sea . . .

Dover – Calais

James Arthur Jones

One for the Road in the Port of Dover

Under the cliff resides a ghost, its presence terrifies me into a run. The landlord's massive alsatian is sprawled in front of the now defunct fire. Always make it to Dover for lasts. A cold night, lie in in the morning.

A hot night, wake up with sea salt in my hair. Another hot night, wind blew through the spokes, woke up with the bike tied to me feet. A long night, wait wait wait. Walk the promenade and the shingle rustles in the curved bay. The hovercraft doesn't run now but its concrete landing bay whispers. The night, another night when this and time were real.

You give me a ride and take my duty-free. Sat in the bar with a sign that reads *North (Wales)*. Six feet of snow. There are things only I know, a half dead pigeon drifts toward the pavement. Faire Cherbourg, 110. St Malo – Salisbury. Dunkerque – border – don't know. Dover Calais Dover – more times than I can remember. Folkestone – Boulogne – Boulogne – Folkestone – National Express

Roscoff – Portsmouth – Southampton – St Malo.
Le Havre. Dieppe a 3h de matin nonpareil. Cinq Ports?! Il eu-plein.

A ride on the hovercraft is like doing 80 down the rumble-strip. Once and once only have I thrown up on the craft, ship, boat, floating thing and that was Calais – Dover. Salerno. Tunis. Tourist Marseille. Martille Tunis. Algeria – Tangier. Tangier Algeria Gib. Harwich – Hook. Hull – Zeebrugge & another for the road in the last of Dover.

The Ghost

So now sitting, Monday morning twelve noon. Sun's shining though the mist's just cleared over the hill. The sign opposite by the churchyard encourages me, and the rest of the world, to Visit Historic Dover. Do they know about the ghost? I don't dare introduce that to the town for fear of incarceration in a padded van. But I know what was there – sober as a judge and wired to fuck, hypersensitive maybe, I don't know, but I do know. I can feel it now, even here a good half-mile away, it's not a benign ghost.

I may have a keener deeper relationship with the town than many of its residents. Their unknown 24 hour street open-air town always pierced by herring gulls. That down there is the real square, the shit pub, the closed pub in the night, the underpass. The shingle rumble suck.

Could have brought everything and all, no return ticket again. Under the vapour trails the sky of Dover and Calais burns orange. I'm depressed but know now I think that this hiatus I have to do. Late train if poss demain and now to the Med, always.

Illustration: Joana Batista

Wash, maybe. Eat, probably. Sun boils orange the clouds, I begin to realise that constant regret in the rear view mirror is both a) fruitless and b) no longer what's needed, but one thing is sure: I am here and they are there.

No longer on the road to the Port of Dover, the First and Last is barricaded over. And with this finally the excuses are gone.

In the Sun on the Other Boat

The river laps around the lion's head flood outlets, storm drains. I came here first off a plane from Africa and the cold is unreal, the march, for the first time for me, to stop (the) war. Afterwards on this deck I met a man from Zim. Now the guy who works here is from Zim.

'Hey mate. He'll be dead soon.'

'Here's hoping.'

What's the first thing I do... hit the road for the Port of Dover, it was all that I could think I'd find familiar. Antwerp. Juke box, flat grey brown fields. Brassica dead heads.

In Calais the CRS aren't too gentle, till you swear at them in French, tell them you've got a ticket (bollox) and a passport. They're out to hunt you into submission. Round the docks the Yugoslav doctors are still there. Nobody knows who these people are, or cares why they are there; in a word, unwanted, either here or where they came from. Gull's screech, toilets' stench and a headwind down the passport control. Calais – Dover. Chinook overhead makes the bench vibrate. The shingle, moonlit, rolls gently behind the waves, reassuring. Over to the left the fridge trucks hum, the cliffs shine bright white. The ghost is yet unknown. The pub is out of reach, the spliff feels well-earned and the pebbles' roll Sisyphean. Perhaps each is a human soul?

Later in the year the waves fly spray into the slate grey sky over the breakwater, the statue to the dead of some half-remembered conflict stares mute into the foam. The castle, as yet unbroached by the brood (I wished) sits, steams, decomposes like a great pile of Staffy dog-shit on the edge of vision. The ghost as yet unknown is.

Somewhere in those cliffs is a honeycomb, a rabbit-warren, England's Last Defence, a poorly lit hole with poorly paid gunners and nurses shitting themselves bombed-out and looking at the red orange glow 23 miles away and waiting for the shell to fall, or not.

The museum is shut. The Wetherspoons is open. Sitting at the bar is like watching the tide, but we all know this anyhow.

Come out south hit the artery, walk five miles, till three in the morning. Chemical plant says Hello France, the wind's edge blows the plume horizontal, one, two, three, four in the morning. No home, no room, no hopes of one. But one, two, three, four coffees, three a.m. give up. Can't get back to the Port of Dover.

Five a.m., lights on, woke up from non-sleep back by the side of the road, why? Because the road is the only thing.

The ghost ran through my bones to the marrow. I ran, almost screaming, back to the secure rustle of the stones. These things aren't possible, ought only to be revealed to the mad.

I say ghost because there are no other words.

What is What was?

Rye is a world of clotted cream and joy. Sweeping seagulls, boats clattering in the creek, wind slaps around the ropes, they aren't much more than string. There is a possibility of the distant hum of a nuclear power station. We, on the bus from Dover to Bexhill are hungry enough to see sheep like steaks on Rammey Marsh. Stinking of strong beer, to meet the in-laws for the first time. Back from Tobacco Road, via the blockhouse and fire. So the smell is Old Speck and petrol and smoke and salt and sand and one for the road in the Port of Dover.

Green Grow the Rushes

Owen Booth

Burton is drunk again and explaining astral projection to the barmaid. It's Friday night and the tiny, one-room pub is half empty. Burton is telling the barmaid about the impossibly thin thread that ties her to this mortal realm, and about the wonders we could all experience if we could only shake ourselves loose of our attachment to this mundane version of reality.

'Dawn breaks behind the eyes,' he tells her – he's quoting now, his hand on hers, leaning across the bar, and, oh, that *voice* - 'From pole of skull and toe, the windy blood slides like a sea . . . '

It's not the first time he's used this approach. It may not even be the first time with this particular barmaid. In the three weeks they've been filming in this forgotten town in the middle of the marshes, the twenty-five-year-old Burton has managed to seduce two schoolgirls, a postmistress, a fifty five year old widower, a landlord's wife – and at least four barmaids. He's also started five fights, crashed two cars, been barred from three pubs and performed Hamlet at four in the morning to a field full of surprised cows.

Burton, it's obvious to everyone even this far from civilisation, is bound for fame. Bound for something, anyway, thinks Livesey, sitting at the other end of the bar with a pale ale and a two day old copy of the Times crossword. God knows, the country could use some of Burton's energy, his optimism, his frightening appetites.

The film they're working on is a sub-Ealing comedy about a town full of Kent smugglers trying to maintain their independence in the face of post-war government bureaucracy. It's a fairly obvious knock-off of *Whisky Galore!* via *Passport to Pimlico*, but it's work, and most of the cast have large tax bills to pay.

Livesey, forty five, veteran of more productions than he can remember, is the film's comic relief and accidental moral centre. Livesey does moral centredness, decency, rectitude, self-deprecating *uprightness* better than just about any Englishman alive. Two days ago three men from the Ministry for the Advancement of the National Character visited the set. Each wearing an identical bowler hat, and carrying an identical umbrella and briefcase. They interviewed Livesey over a cup of twice-stewed tea.

'And the character you play in the film, this . . . '

'Captain Biddle.'

'Captain Biddle. A smuggler and divorcee. A frequently drunk smuggler and divorcee, in fact. Is he, would you say, representative of the sort of values that England needs at this time?'

'I suppose that would depend on who you asked.'

'Well, we're rather asking you Mister Livesey.'

Livesey knows their sort very well, these shabby, grey men. They're the same types who tried to stop them filming *The Life and Death of Colonel Blimp* in 1943. 'Potentially injurious to the national mood at a time of great peril,' was the consensus. Because the film

Illustration: Joe Becci

dared to suggest that history was a fractious, troublesome sea, and that a certain strain of backward-looking Englishness was about to be drowned in the surf.

'It's 1951, Mr Livesey,' his interviewers told him, sipping their tea, smoking their pipes, ticking off entries on their lists. 'We've lost an empire. Our country is in ruins. We'll be paying off the debt to the Americans for the next fifty years. Never mind the war: this, now, is our true darkest hour. Now more than ever we need performances that fortify the public mood.'

Before they left they asked him to sign their forms in triplicate. They gave him a copy for his records.

Livesey is just about thinking of calling it a night and heading back to the chalet, when the Burton pulls up a stool next to him. He looks ready to burst with excitement. He can't even meet Livesey's eyes.

'I've found a man who can take us Liv,' Burton says.

'Take us where, Rich?' says Livesey

'Come on Livesey . . . '

Livesey knows where. Burton has been talking about it for days.

'Don't you want to know the secrets of life and death?' he says.

'You know: I'm not sure I do,' says Livesey. 'I'm fairly certain there are things we're not meant to understand.'

Burton lights a cigarette, keeping his eyes on the barmaid. His hand shakes ever so slightly.

'I need you Roger,' – it's the first time Livesey can remember him using his first name – 'I need an anchor. I need a witness. What if I'm unable to get back from the other side?'

And isn't there something in the lad's aching wildness, right there, that reminds him of himself, or of how he could have turned out? The Livesey who was born in the back of a travelling theatre, somewhere out in the black Welsh countryside, showbusiness in his blood and bone . . .

Livesey sighs, puts down his paper. 'Who is it?' he asks.

Burton takes a long drag and nods towards the ancient fisherman resting two fingers on top of a glass of gin at the other end of the bar. He's the oldest living being Livesey has ever seen.

'Can he even see?' whispers Livesey.

'Don't need to see,' announces the old man before looking up. Then he lifts his head and meets Livesey's gaze with milky white eyes. '*Mister* Livesey.'

Livesey, the gent, raises his glass to the old man.

***

Six hundred and fifty years ago this was one of the most important ports on the English Channel. Then half the town was dragged out to sea by a storm that silted up the harbour overnight and shifted the course of the river two miles down the coast. After that people had to find alternative ways to make a living. They say that as long as you can put a price on it, someone on the marsh can get it for you. Nylons. Napoleon Brandy. Nuclear secrets. Arcane knowledge.

It's one in the morning and Burton and Livesey are sitting in the back of the mariner's open boat as he navigates the reed-choked, salt-poisoned waterways. Livesey is trying to work out their position from the stars but the mist keeps obscuring the sky. Wrapped up in his coat he's wondering, once again, how he got dragged into this, how he's going to get Burton home in one piece. Burton, most likely, is thinking about one of the wardrobe girls, the script girl, the director's assistant. Anyone but his wife.

The boatman, hand on the tiller, is inscrutable. He is steering by memory.

Then Burton pipes up.

'Tell me,' he says, in the darkness, over the sound of the puttering outboard motor, 'do you believe in the survival of human personality after death?'

'That sounds like a familiar line,' says Livesey.

'It's you. *A Matter of Life and Death*. Kim Hunter says "I don't know, I've never thought about it". And your character says – '

'My character says "I don't know, I've thought about it too much".'

'But do you?' says Burton. 'Believe?'

'Do you know what my favourite line from that film is?' asks Livesey. '"A weak mind isn't strong enough to hurt itself. Stupidity has saved many a man from going mad." I rather think that might be my entire philosophy of life. In a nutshell, as it were.'

Burton goes quiet again. After a few minutes they pass the remains of an old wooden landing stage. 'Wait,' he says, 'pull up here.'

'Oh, surely not?' says Livesey.

'A candle in the thighs warms youth and seed!' announces Burton as they steer towards the bank, 'And burns the seeds of age!' Then he hops out, scrambling to the raised road. He is momentarily silhouetted against the starry sky. 'If I'm not back in ten minutes, send reinforcements,' he says. And then he heads off towards the dark shape of a farmhouse some two hundred yards down the road, where a single window is lit up like a beacon.

In the night's silence Livesey and the ancient boatman consider each other.

'Smoke?' says Livesey.

The old man takes a cigarette, breaking off the filter and throwing it away, and leans forward for a light. Livesey catches a whiff of river mud, rotten fish, something indefinable.

'Cold night,' says Livesey. His palms are starting to sweat.

The old man stares at him. His skin is the clammy texture of tripe, like he's been left underwater for a week. Somewhere out on the marshes a bird hoots. Frogs call. A muffled splash.

There are things murdering each other all around us, Livesey thinks.

Then there's the inevitable, impossibly loud crash of a shotgun blast, and here's Burton coming hareing back along the road, his white shirt bobbing in the darkness.

'Start the engine!' he's shouting. 'Start the damn engine!'

The old boatman doesn't wait. They're already a good ten feet away by the time Burton reaches the bank, and he has to throw himself into the water and swim after them. In the darkness his cuckolded pursuer fires off another couple of random shots as the low mist folds in around them. Livesey manages to get hold of Burton's jacket and pull him aboard, half drowned.

He lies there in the bottom of the boat laughing. They steer out into the deeper water.

***

According to the retired schoolmaster with whom Livesey has been playing chess every Tuesday and Thursday night since they started filming, this has always been an unreliable landscape. Whole villages have been known to disappear overnight – their residents taken by the sea, or the Black Death, vague things that no one wants to talk about. Now there are rumours of strange government comings and goings out beyond the giant concrete acoustic mirrors on Dungeness headland. Of the night time arcing of mysterious power sources across the salt lagoons. Of submarines and medical experiments and fishermen landing secret cargos.

On the marsh, rumours are currency.

They hear the stranded barge before they see it. Sitting on its sandbank it creaks and moans against the rush of the incoming tide like something half alive. Then the midnight black bulk of it looms over them, blocking out the light from the stars.

There's a figure too, leaning out from the deck. Behind him the milky way wheels.

'Is that Malcolm Barnes?' the man shouts. The wind is getting up.

'It is,' the boatman shouts back.

'And who's that with you, Malcolm Barnes?'

'None but two seekers of the truth,' shouts Burton, attempting to stand up in the rocking boat. There's a chop on the water now and the wind is ruffling his hair. 'In search of esoteric wisdom.'

'Esoteric, is it?' shouts the man on deck. 'Well, you'd better come up then'

He rolls down a rope ladder. Livesey and Burton haul themselves up onto the muddy deck.

As they struggle to their feet their host, dressed in black oilskins, his face obscured by a cowl, holds up a lantern and studies them. Then, he directs them to go below decks.

The cabin is lit by a single oil lamp. The walls are lined with the skeletons and shells of hundreds of unidentifiable sea creatures, as well as faded photographs and paintings of degenerate men and women. The stench of rotten wood is a wet, living thing. It slithers into Burton and Livesey's lungs with the first breath, and makes itself at home. Everything has a sheen of salt. A kaleidoscope of mineral stalactites hang from the beams.

Three men sit at a table. They have the same drowned pallor as the ancient boatman. Each is wearing an old, badly shrunk suit and a filthy seaman's cap to which are pinned a crab, a fish and some sort of frog. The dried, dead things stare at the newcomers with glassy eyes. Livesey watches as a worm wriggles from the fish's mouth and drops onto the table.

The first man gestures for Burton and Livesey to approach.

'Time was,' he says, 'when half the trade from France used to come through these waters. And men lived like kings. But the sea giveth and the sea taketh away. Wouldn't you say so, sirs?'

'Though they go mad they shall be sane,' says Burton, agreeing. 'Though they sink through the sea they shall rise again.'

'That's it exactly,' says the man. Livesey has the strangest feeling he's met this fellow before. 'Empires rise and fall. The waters of commerce roll on. And a pair of young men like yourselves come looking for – '

He stops and squints at Livesey.

'No,' he says. 'Just one of you then?

Livesey can't help noticing that the other two men have their eyes fixed on the worm winding and unwinding on the table before them. One of them slowly runs a blue tongue across his lips.

'I have money,' says Burton.

'Of course you have,' says their interrogator. 'But be aware that getting the information you seek may not necessarily give you what you need.'

'That's what I tried to tell him,' says Livesey.

The man looks at Livesey again, as if trying to place him. Then his eyes slip past him to the cabin door. The man in the oilskins enters, followed by the sound of the rising wind.

'Our foreign friends have arrived,' he announces.

Out of the corner of his eye, Livesey sees one of the other two men grab the worm from the table and stuff it into his mouth.

***

The wind has cleared away the last of the mist and the stars are riding high above the rushing clouds as the little boat makes its way back up the river in the hours before dawn.

Livesey, sitting up front, has never seen a sky so vast, or felt so insignificant. He thinks of the night time test flights out of Desford Aerodrome during the war, looking out of the bomb doors at ten thousand feet and knowing they were passing over entire blacked-out, dreaming cities.

Burton is catatonic. He had smoked the stuff the Russian sailors brought with them. They had to take him off the barge in the end. He was shouting about drowned villages, ghosts of fishermen, the imminent return of a great, vengeful water god. When he'd claimed to be able to see future and past simultaneously.

'Broken ghosts with glow-worms in their heads!' Burton insisted as they bundled him into the boat. 'The things of light file through the flesh where no flesh decks the bones!'

It occurs to Livesey that if Burton doesn't snap out of it soon, he's going to have a very hard time explaining the evening's events to the director.

'I saw my mother,' murmurs Burton, his eyes still fixed on

infinity. 'She was waiting for me.'

'I know she was old chap,' says Livesey, patting the young man's hand.

Under cover of darkness they coast towards the landing at the edge of town, the boatman cutting the engine and using a pole to punt them the last hundred yards. In the grey light they lift the uncomprehending Burton onto the wooden dock.

'That's that then,' says the boatman.

Livesey reaches for his wallet, realises Burton is wearing his coat. 'How much do we owe you for the rental?' he asks

'Never said it was my boat,' says old Malcolm Barnes, and then leaps into the water. With a single splash, a kick of his legs, he's gone. He doesn't resurface.

Livesey, exhausted, sits down on the dock and lifts Burton's wide-eyed, dreaming head into his lap. He reaches past him, inside the coat for his crumpled packet of cigarettes, lights one, and ponders the immensity of the flat landscape as the day starts to wash in around them. Slowly the marsh turns from black and white to technicolour.

He knows what Burton saw.

He can see them himself, hundreds of them out among the rushes, fishermen and farmers and smugglers in ranks going back for centuries. He relives superimposed catastrophes of one storm after another, each reshaping the landscape. He watches towns and villages grow and die, sand and sea reclaiming everything. It's an old actor's tick, this facility for understanding places, tuning into ancient frequencies. On The Life and Death of Colonel Blimp, filmed in the middle of the war, it nearly killed him, finding himself the channel for the wounded, desperate voices of fifty million people.

He knows what they're building out on the shingle at Dungeness too; understands, somehow, that it means the death of whatever old gods have been squatting on the marsh for the last few thousand years. From now on the only human sacrifices will be in the name of energy security, economic development, improved transport links.

Livesey finishes his cigarette and thinks about the poem that Burton keeps quoting. He still can't make much sense of it.

'The secret of the soil grows through the eye and blood jumps in the sun,' he says to the ghosts out on the marsh. 'Above the waste allotments the dawn halts.'

For a hundred years in either direction nobody hears a thing.

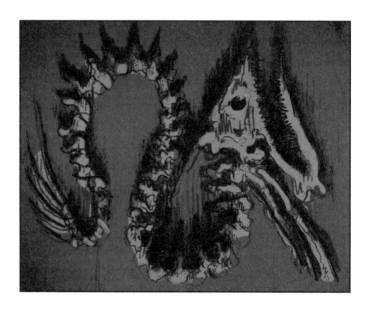

IV

Hastings

Thunderbird Caravan

Salena Godden

On the train from Ashford to Hastings
you will pass yellow fields
lily pond and tuft and matted sheep
as you approach Ham Street
you'll notice a pig farm
a line of tin roof shacks
that you cannot mistake
but I did
I fell in love there once
I was up to the neck in the swill
we lived in that rusting, mildewed caravan
and we showered there
under a hose in that very meadow
whilst piglets snuffled in our hay bale furniture
the sky and the time was summer
we had bonfires and we had Neil Young

we drank Thunderbirds under naked starlight
I was skinny and barefoot and wild
I was slapped and I got bruised and pregnant
I was sixteen and cocksure
but I had no idea how to come or go
until I ran away one dark night
through fields of corn
I was once the prodigal daughter
shivering in the station
waiting for dawn train
never knowing that years later
I'd be on a train to Hastings
leaning out of the window
looking for the pig farm
remembering
the sting of young love
remembering harvest
a man needs a maid
are you ready for the country
heart of gold
the needle and the damage
done.

Corridor Assassins

Aziza Abdullah

There's confusion in the air, mixed with salt and tarmac and all that bloody dog poo.

It's not mind-blowing, more gliding from pebble to post and realigning pillars and posts . . .

Recovering from being stuck behind a Sunday driver on the single lane section of the A21 I enjoyed the pomp and pageantry with the best view – St Mary in the Castle, Pelham Place where they burn celebrity effigies and their failing youth, exclaiming 'off with their hoodz'.

You'd better watch out, the out-of-towners are coming back to town (as if I didn't know).

I smelled her before I met her and still I held her hand and pulled her up to share my view.

She had not yet been to the Jerwood for fear of bumping into people she once knew.

Chance encounters with old classmates who'd look down on and through her, she explained.

Besides, passing observations through the window had told her all she needed to know.

On her way to the off-licence, marvelling at the sky's cloud formation; gold and silver lines.

Far beyond the ghostly skeleton frame, joggers, wind surfers, burger and ice-cream vans.

Somewhere over the vast grey matter and beyond the multicoloured distant landmass.

She once played with boys and double-barrelled finger guns along a shiny school corridor.

Aiming at relative strangers in a valley of little people who'd been asked to leave their class.

Punished for disrupting progress then turning on each other out of boredom and for fun.

Rumours of Riots

Christian Watson

Fear, or boredom.

My first hint was a phone call from Grace.

'We're closing early,' she said. 'The police have told us there could be riots.'

I rubbed my eye, 'Shit,' I said as it began to sting. The paint made me blink, my sight blurred with tears. 'When did they tell you that?'

'The police didn't tell us, they told the people at Eat Café. Stephanie went in there earlier and they passed it on. They're telling all local businesses.'

'The police are telling people there are going to be riots?' I had been painting all day. My contact with the world had consisted of a short trip to Sainsbury's for rations. I scanned the headlines. Riots were a distant event, nothing to do with me. You can't riot against the sea, against open space. Riots are hemmed in, close-quartered affairs against a backdrop of bricks, concrete and glass, not the horizon, gulls, lapping waves, a burnt out pier and pebbles by the million. I continued to blink, my eye stinging, rubbing at my socket with my paint-free palm.

'The police are saying it's probably going to happen. Turners has closed early. Steph is leaving early. I think I'm going to stay here.' Grace said this like she was reporting the weather. For the last five years she'd lived in Manchester, coming down to Hastings to get away from the city, to take photographs and build a portfolio without the abundant distractions of the big city. She was always complaining of being bored, but she couldn't fault the rent.

I didn't believe riots could find a spark in the salt-heavy air of Hastings, but that didn't matter. Fear and boredom are as dangerous as anger in the right hands.

'Are you going to be alright?' I asked. I knew Grace could look after herself, she had spent her years at university walking alone in the pre-dawn hours wearing not much more than smudged lipstick, but I had to ask. 'I'll be at work in an hour, so if you want to hold off finishing until then you can come to The Albion, it's only down the road.'

'No, I'll be alright,' she said. 'I don't think anything is going to happen, it's just weird, everyone's talking about it like the riots are a real person. Like a storm or something. I think it's funny.'

'It sounds ridiculous,' I said. 'What are they going to loot? Charity shops and pound stores? Or maybe they have their eye on the Jerwood. I know there's plenty of people looking for an excuse to burn that to the ground.'

'Yeah, get it before it's finished, they'd dance around the fire like it was bonfire night, all the fishermen playing with sparklers. I like sparklers, especially when it's old men playing with them. Oh, I hope it happens now.'

It was hard for Grace to stay serious for long, especially when the subject felt so silly to begin with.

'It won't,' I said. 'But we can get some sparklers, if you want, we don't have to wait until bonfire night.'

'Then they wouldn't be special.'

We talked for a bit more on the subject of nothing much, the conversation ending with hurried declarations of love. I looked out of a broken window towards the sea, searching the horizon scattered with the low, black shapes of ships scudding through the channel. All that's needed for a scene is actors, enough people willing to believe in the fiction. I knew from living in this town these last few years that there was enough will for something, anything to happen. Drama comes easily to those with little danger to worry them. But riots? I couldn't see it.

I pulled my gas-mask back down over my face, taking one last look at the sea. I was still blinking from the paint. My sight was drawn from the horizon to the burnt out pier that protruded into the blue, a blackened splinter decaying against the shore. It was the kind of day that made Hastings worth living in, where the sea and sky were both as still as each other, not a cloud or wave to break them apart. I turned away, focused again on the piece I was painting, picking up the spray-can.

Arriving with my family in Hastings, I'd been disappointed by the opportunities on offer for a quiet graffiti artist. I preferred painting in abandoned buildings than out in the open, and though there were many empty shops with whitewashed windows hung with 'To Let' signs, there was no way into them. The Observer building, with its crumbling, post-Victorian façade, boarded up windows, and dark stains of water damage, drew me towards it like a moth to a bare bulb. Compared to the carefully crafted façade, the back of the building was all exposed guts. The windows I could reach were boarded up, but I found that, by risking a few broken bones, I could climb up a rusting drainpipe, shimmy across a ledge no wider than my fingertips, pull myself up another pipe that was loosely moored to the wall by rusting brackets, reach up to the rotting wood of a third story windowsill and drag myself in.

I was at ease with the sound of roosting pigeons, dripping water, a thousand chances to contract tetanus. What interested me was not the dank staircases and echoing spaces of the open-plan floors, but the walls; all of them flat and bare save for the damp dust and peeling layers of ancient paint.

By the time I had finished painting for the day the rumours seemed as unreal as the riots themselves. I packed up my cans and gas-mask, looking again out over the rooftops of Hastings, out to the Channel. The vast space always gave me a feeling of being on the edge of the world, the town one wrong-foot away from being swept into nothing, another corpse to be fished from the waves by the coastguard. I took in the silver sweep of the sun reflecting off the sleep-calm sea, blinking the brightness back, watched a gull land on the head of one of the tall lampposts that lined the seafront. To riot against this would be throwing our names into a void. We build shelters to protect ourselves from such places. We don't burn them. The sea reflects flames and swallows warmth.

On the way to work I encountered the same aimless fear Grace had brought to my attention. I dumped my paint-stained bag at home and walked down to Scoffers to get a pizza. The paint fumes still buzzing in my head made it easy to marvel at the sun cutting clear shadows at near perfect 45 degree angles. The streets half aglow, half in shade.

Down the Brassey Steps, as I arrived at Scoffers, I was hailed by Bill on his bike. We stopped for a chat. Bill was a worn hipster, eyes permanently hidden behind a pair of wraparound sunglasses. By way of greeting Bill said, 'Have you seen anything kicking off?'

Illustration: Craig John-Barr

I worked my way back through the memory of my walk but couldn't find anything that fit Bill's description. 'Why?' I asked, 'Have you? What's happening?'

'There's riots supposed to be kicking off, outside McDonalds.' Bill sat back on his saddle, my perplexed reflection looking back at me from his sunglasses. 'I just came from the Old Town to see if it was alright.'

'I haven't seen anything.' Outside McDonalds? It's where teenagers hang out, but there isn't much to riot with; a few benches, a couple of litter bins, one of those boxes full of worn flowers that clutter pedestrianised areas across the country. I tried to reassure Bill. 'Nothing will happen, it's just rumours.'

Behind his sunglasses Bill's eyes were inscrutable. 'Yeah, I know, there's been some strange stuff going on. Kids from the local schools have been getting text messages from numbers they don't know about meeting up places to kick off. The police have been telling people to close early and keep out of town. Celia is afraid to bring her kids though town in case something happens. I'm just checking it out, having a look round to make sure it's safe.'

Bill was one of the most laid back people I knew, often with a spliff hanging from the corner of his mouth. Most of our conversations up until now had revolved around music. 'Where'd you hear about the text messages?'

'Just some mates' kids,' said Bill, looking around and past me. 'Apparently they are planning to attack Morrisons, they've got police up there now.'

'Morrisons? Really? This is ridiculous. Do you think it's going to happen?'

'I don't know, I don't think so. I mean, what's to riot for in Hastings? There's barely enough people to fill a decent gig, never mind burn the place down.'

'Yeah, I guess. Speaking of gigs, are you playing The Pig on Saturday?'

'Yeah, yeah, man. It'll be a good night. You and Grace coming down?'

'Probably, if I don't get looted first.'

Bill laughed. 'Yeah, well, it sounds funny, but it's still worrying. Anyway, I've gotta go. If I see anything I'll text you. Catch you later, man.'

'Laters. Be careful.'

Bill waved and pedaled away on his low-rider, his insect legs pumping a searching rhythm, black hair flapping in the wind, shades firmly in place. Another body on the streets looking for a fight to avoid.

In Scoffers the muted TV hung in the corner, playing scenes from last night's riots, showing kids in tracksuits with covered faces smashing windows and running out of stores with arms full, running towards the camera and out of shot. I thought about what Bill had said, tried to put myself in the position of a teenager sent a text message urging me to riot. On the television, with the sound muted, it looked like a lot of fun.

Hastings, if you discount the odd stabbing, is not a violent place. I had never felt unsafe walking the streets, after Bradford. It was boring but I thanked my parents for moving here. Walking Bradford at night the threat of violence was real. Every night the helicopter was out, searchlight chasing some stolen car, sweeping the landscape as sirens shrieked through the night. Bradford, crouched in its valley, houses upon houses, smoke stacks and terraced rows on every horizon, was a trap, like being squeezed in a fist of dirt and stone. Hastings, stretched lazily along the coast, no pressure, only the peripheral fear of falling off, of being lost, forgotten. Hastings and Bradford; suicide and murder.

I took my pizza for a walk along the seafront and found a bench to sit on as I ate. By the second slice the gulls congregated by my feet. There were three in front, heads bobbing and cawing between each other, their eyes eager for pizza. I kept the lid closed between slices and read my book, not quite taking it in. A group of young lads sat down at one of the picnic benches behind me. It was when I heard the word 'riot' that I began to listen.

'If a riot kicks off yeah, call me, I'll be down for the looting, trust me.'

'Did you see it on TV? They were running out with plasma screen TV's and bare new trainers, there was brand new kicks lying on the pavement there were that many of 'em bruv.'

'Trust me bruv, it's all kicking off, it's intense.'

'Up there yoots're taking over, it's crazy, they're shanking men, soon we'll be in control.'

'You've gotta take the opportunity while you can bruv, get it while you can.'

'Did you see it in Ealing Buv? They burned down a whole Sony depot, a whole block.'

'They could've got enough out of that place bruv, enough Playstations.'

'Kev is going up there with his cousin, they've taken a van, he says it'll be like shopping.'

'I've got to go up home first bruv, but give us a call if it kicks off, I'll be straight down for the looting.'

'Well, nah, wait up a minute, give it five minutes and we'll all go up, there's no point waiting round town.'

Yeah bruv, there's no point hanging around, wait 'til it kicks off and then get down here.'

I threw the final pizza crust to the gulls. There was the obligatory scuffle before the crust was gulped down by the biggest, its aggressive bulk leaving the others without a chance. Those gulls left with nothing began to loudly craw at me. I picked up my empty pizza box, glanced behind me and saw four lads with short hair in jeans, tracksuits and hooded tops. They were sat around the table, heads bobbing like the gulls at my feet, waiting for something to happen.

When I arrived at work, the first thing James – fellow barman and professional cynic – said to me was, 'So you didn't bring your riot gear then?'

'Should I have?' I asked, taking in the empty bar as I removed my coat.

'There's rumours of riots all over the old town.' James pulled himself a pint of Landlord. 'Turners has closed, a few other places have closed early, and none of the regulars have come in. It's tense.'

I couldn't hide my amusement. 'Yeah, I noticed the old boys weren't propping up the bar, I thought the fisherman's club was doing a meat raffle. Nothing is going to happen, but it would be nice to finish early.'

'No chance of that,' said James around a mouthful of ale. 'Alistair wouldn't close this place if it was on fire, he'd have you pulling pints for the fireman and charging those watching for the privilege.'

'You been in here on your own all day? Where's Alistair?'

'He's in hiding upstairs, probably making some sort of fortress. I've heard him pacing, surprised he hasn't worn a hole in the ceiling. He came down earlier, clucking worse than usual. I don't know why he's bothered, he'd probably be happier with the insurance money.'

I nodded in agreement. Even on a busy night we were lucky to get a handful of people in after the regulars went home. As much as he wouldn't admit it, it was Alistair's fault; he was rude to the tourists, wouldn't let children in the pub, and had some long running spat with most of the locals. If you asked him what the problem was he'd blame everything from the smoking ban to the government's immigration policy.

'Are you rioting tonight, then?' I asked James as he finished off the last of his pint.

'Not me, I've got a hot date with a spliff and *Call of Duty*. Mind you, if they loot Game I might go down and see if I can grab a couple of new controllers, I'm sure mine are wearing out.'

'No, you're just getting old, your reactions are slipping. If you see anything on your way home send us a text, I could do with a laugh.'

'Will do.'

I was alone in the bar. Alistair shouted down the stairs for me to bring in the street furniture, 'Just in case.' I proceeded to clean all the tables and bar tops, wipe the glass on the fridge, clean the mirror and wipe all the ashtrays. By the time I finished I still hadn't served a customer. I leant against the bar and started reading.

It was dark outside when Alistair came down the stairs. He didn't greet me. 'Who are those people outside? Are they paying customers?'

'What people?' I asked.

'Those people sat outside on the benches.'

I looked out of the window to where Alistair was pointing. Sat outside was a group of six teenagers. One of them looked like he was drinking. They were sat around the benches talking quietly.

'I haven't served any of them a drink.'

'What are they doing out there?'

'They look like they're sat down.' I wasn't sure where this line of questioning was going. Teenagers often sat on the benches outside. 'They'll probably be gone in a minute,'

'I don't feel safe with them outside. I've been listening from the window, I'm sure I heard them say the police were on them or something like that. I think they're up to something. I'd feel a lot safer if they weren't there.' Alistair moved his head like gulls vying for pizza crusts, his hands making worried pecking motions in the air.

'Considering all the rumours tonight, I'd feel a lot safer not getting into a confrontation with people who, left to their own devices, are going to move away in a minute.' Any other day I would have done as Alistair asked and got rid of the teenagers. They were not staying, I could see it in their stance, three of them were standing and looking into the distance, hands in their pockets. They were waiting for something to happen. Alistair was waiting for something to happen. I was not going to be the catalyst for someone else's drama.

Alistair took the phone off the cradle and went in the back room. I carried on reading, occasionally looking out of the window. With each look the group looked nearer to moving on. Two more stood up. Then they were all standing. Next time I looked up they had dispersed like gas, moving off in the same vague direction. I went in the back to tell Alistair and he was on the phone, ' . . . yes, a few were wearing tracksuits and one of them had ginger hair . . . ' I went back to my book.

Alistair put the phone back on the cradle. He leaned against the bar, chin pointing towards me. 'The police have them on CCTV and are watching them and don't think they look right, and I don't think they look right. I've been listening to them. I think they were looking for trouble.'

He kept peeking out of the window, going from the back to the front door. I left him to his delusions of apocalypse and went back to my book.

A woman came into the pub. I vaguely recognised her as local. She wore shorts cut off at her mottled thigh, face a layer of sweaty make up. Her head had that slight loll that lets you know the drink you're serving isn't the first of the night. She started talking to Alistair about rumours of riots while she stirred her wine and soda with a straw.

'I heard they attacked Morrisons,' she said, looking into her drink as if there was something missing. She looked up at Alistair who was wide eyed and eager for the worst. 'Yeah, twelve of them, I heard. They ran in trying to cause trouble but nothing happened. The police were on them too quick. But it's terrible, it's happening everywhere.'

'I knew something would happen.' Alistair looked at me as he said this. I sprayed anti-bacterial cleaner onto the bar top and began to wipe. 'These kids are terrible today, no respect for anyone or anything. It's been awful watching the telly. Someone should do something. They should all be round up and shot.'

'Oh yes.' The woman gulped her drink. 'It doesn't bear thinking of, all of them lot running up and down the street. I live alone, on my own, Brian is away all week, and you don't get no signal down there, I couldn't phone anyone.'

'What if they were to torch your house?'

'Oh, I don't want to think about it, I hope nothing does happen. I don't know what I'd do. I've worked hard for my money, Alistair, I have, and it's not been easy, I've had to work everyday.

These kids want something for nothing, all on a plate like it was Christmas, like it was all free. Did you see Turners was closed?'

'Oh, I know, they closed up earlier today. It's terrible, people with real jobs and businesses. I can't imagine what I'd do if someone burned this place down.' Alistair sipped his drink carefully. 'Actually, I can. I'd move to Whitby, away from here, get a nice B&B. Give me half a chance, I'd be off.'

'Oh, that would be nice, I want to move to Cornwall but Brian says it would be harder for work. I can't see how it would be harder than round here, there's nothing. Nice up there in Whitby, friendlier by far. Not like down here with all those bloody London lot. Turners was closed as soon as the police had been around, scared of being looted, and that's no way to run a business, how are you supposed to make a living? I noticed the post office didn't close. That Paki wouldn't close for the end of the world, the money grubbing bastard that he is.'

'I know, I know,' nodded a sycophantic Alistair. He asked me for another wine and soda and one for the lady. My only input into the conversation was to keep the alcohol flowing. I was happy to keep it that way. It was a good book.

'That's terrible about Morrisons,' said Alistair sipping from a fresh drink. 'These kids have no respect for anyone. Bring back National Service, I say, give them all a bit of discipline. What can they get from Morrisons? The only reason I go there is to get my toiletries. When they're on buyonegetonefree I stock up, especially that toothpaste . . . '

Alistair and the woman continued to exchange tips on where best to bulk buy when the bargains are on. I wasn't reading my book. I couldn't concentrate as my mind went over the implications of the conversation. Was this happening all over town? Was there, in every bar along George Street, a small group of locals huddled in fear, sharing rumours and prejudice whilst fearing the worst? How had this happened? I'd seen the headlines, seen the pictures of youths with faces covered, framed by a backdrop of flames and broken windows. So distant from these quiet streets and salt-worn bricks. I saw boredom, desperation to be involved in some grand narrative.

Hastings had been plagued by rumours of riots before, in the 60s. In Brighton, bored youths wearing the disparate uniforms of almost indistinguishable sub-cultures splashed each other's blood on the pebbles while the sea rasped indifferently at the shore. Hastings beach had also been part of the blood-letting, sort of. There was no riot, no property damage. A lot of young people down for the bank holiday had been escorted off the beach by police flown in especially for the occasion. Somehow, the event was dubbed the Battle of Hastings and went down as one of the bloodiest events in local history since the real battle of Hastings, which also, much to the locals chagrin, didn't happen in Hastings.

It was only when I heard the woman saying, 'Bloody Polish think they can do what they want' that I was pulled away from my thoughts.

'You know what they did?' She was still talking to Alistair, her words tumbling over the bar like oddly weighted dominoes. Alistair was nodding, not noticing how awkwardly her phrases landed. 'My Brian was working down Birmingham, well, up, doing a job up there. On contract, agency. He's a good lad our Brian.'

'Oh yeah, lovely feller,' said Alistair.

'We should have moved up there when we had the chance. But we stayed down here, regret it now. And what happened with Brian, well, it was enough to make you, well, the company let him go. Just like that. One day he went in and they told him he wasn't needed.'

'That's terrible,' said Alistair, a mask of concern.

'Well, that wasn't the worst thing. After they let him go, you know what they did? They got a whole load of Polish in there, doing the same job for less money, it's enough to make you sick.'

Alistair nodded in agreement, giving supportive sounds, avidly accepting her every statement. I try to stay out of these conversations that happen around me. In Bradford opinions like this were below the surface of every pint drank in a dim bar. There, it wasn't the Polish.

'Who do you blame?' I asked her.

The woman focused her bleary attention on me for the first time. 'What do you mean?'

'I asked: who do you blame? For Brian being sacked?'

She carried on looking at me, her lips moving to formulate an answer. I carried on, 'Do you blame the Polish for being employed by the company for less money, or do you blame the company for paying the Polish less money for the same job?'

'Well, I blame the government,' she said I began to ask why, when she blurted, 'because they let those bloody Polish into the country in the first place. They shouldn't be here, what's wrong with their country?'

'So you don't blame the company that sacked your Brian and then hired the Polish just so they could save on their overheads?'

'Why would I? If the government hadn't let them in then the company wouldn't employ them. They got them cheaper. Why do they have to come here and take our jobs? They were paying Brian seven pounds an hour. They get them Polish in and they're paying half the wages. Bloody cheek of it, and they send it all home. They can afford it living seven to a house . . . ' And she went on. Alistair nodded like a parcel shelf dog on a bumpy road. The rest of the bar lay silent and empty.

'Whose side are you on, anyway?'

The woman and Alistair were looking at me. It was the woman who had spoken. Alistair had a half grin that told me there was a right and wrong answer to this question.

'I'm on your side,' I said to the woman with an apologetic smile. 'I want your Brian in work. It's not fair that he lost his job to the Polish, and you're right, it is the government's fault, I just don't like people being pushed around. Would you like another drink?'

'Oh, yes dear, that would be lovely.'

I poured them both drinks, sat back and kept silent. When the clock neared eleven I put on my coat, dropped the keys on the bar, said my good nights and walked out without looking back.

Walking along the seafront I looked out towards the sea. I could only make out the horizon from the flashing lights, fishing boats eager for a catch and tankers making their way to and from any number of places I only knew from an atlas. The lights of Hastings dappled close to the shore; there were no flames reflected there. The only sounds the gentle rake of slow waves moving across pebbles, the pulsing of lone cars moving along the road. Looking towards St Leonards I could make out the silhouette of the skeletal pier, the houses along the seafront lit up by the phosphorous glow of the street lights. Everything still and calm.

In my pocket my phone buzzed. It was Grace. I answered it, her first words were her asking if I was okay.

'Yeah, all good, just on my way home now.'

'How's town?' She asked.

'Dead as always, except there's less drunks. There's a few police cruising along the sea front, but they look as bored as I feel. Looks like another Hasting non-event.'

'You should be used to it by now.'

'I'm more than used to it, I count on it. If anything actually happened around here I'd have to move to Bexhill.'

'God's own waiting room,' laughed Grace, who knew better than I, it's where she had grown up. 'Steph phoned me a couple of hours ago, she said Morrisons had been attacked by some lads.'

'I heard the same. If anything it'll just be some lads getting caught shoplifting. Do you want me to pick you up anything on the way home?'

'No, it's alright, I got some wine here and picked up a DVD.'

'I'll be home in ten minutes.'

'Love you,' and she clicked off before I could respond. I had been kicking a pebble as we talked, now I picked it up and felt the weight in my hand. There was fear, fear in every event that bypassed this town. It was the fear of nothing, the great space that confronted Hastings every day. The people of this town filled the sea with all the possibilities it allowed them to imagine, and the sea swallowed them with the indifference that nature has practiced so well in the face of human endeavor. These rumours one more attempt at keeping boredom at bay. A shared myth of what could be, that this town hoped would stop it slipping into obscurity. I pulled my hand back, judging the weight of the pebble I held there, and hurled it at the sea. I listened for the return of a swallowing thunk, but the sound that reached my ears was the sharp skittering of stone on stone, then nothing; the sound of the sea breathing against the shore, waiting.

Seasonal Sobriety

Aziza Abdullah

Freewheeling on lines of distinction, unwelcomed otherness was the topic the sorority decided on and proceeded to spread like homemade jam on last week's challah bread. Their collective mind published pathways to resolutions but had delayed solutions which ended in budget cuts and shortcuts and never amounted to much.

Mina, the leader was idealistic and searched for commonality. She thought they were all connected, she thought wrong and expected camaraderie even when they disagreed. Conjecture on her part, she accepted; perennially eager and on the lookout for that ever-fixed mark in a part they all played in the bigger picture. Tired, she retired, but not without leaving a legacy; Royal Victoria was booked for a talk on local history, a coach to Peasmarsh for a demonstration at Jempson's bakery, numerous parties and openings of exhibitions at all the town's galleries neatly inserted in the group's online diary.

Sometimes they used the same language when talking. When networking, buzzwords flew around the heads of the few who knew how to work the room. One could say they were all walking in the same direction but there's always one who asks a question, doesn't wait for an answer but replies with gunfire aimed at any toes not firmly behind the line.

'But it wasn't a race! Who called it a race then ran for cover to hide her face?' Grace, the oldest one asked gasping for air and pulling out.

'She won't get my vote. Clearly you don't need us old folk.'

Nudging her best friend Zola who choked and awoke, eventually adding, 'Don't let them fool you, there's no prize. You'll always be black in their eyes.'

Gaining momentum she feigned surprise and mockingly screamed, 'Don't look into the light'.

Grace relayed, 'This was once a town with so few I had no group to belong to. Now you battle for the unobtainable because you can't see our joint contribution is vital both as women and artists – Don't take this lightly! We have shared interests in almost everything bar material showboating and cavorting in last chance saloons. This duel is where I draw the line; Mina's gone and it all feels wrong. You mistake decency for complacency and push individual motives as group objectives. In Bar Blah you dance around notions instead of taking things on. Sorry, but I'm moving on.'

The constant gardener was a truism Margaret the landscaper liked to use on female jealousy and other fallacies found in misogynistic mythology, couch psychology and GP surgeries.

She stood up to explain, 'While waiting for smears and scans we're smearing ourselves and each other with scandalous filth excreted from so-called women's magazines, like *10 ways to judge if your man fancies your best friend* and *Never let him mend her car or clear out her garage – Sister, don't go there!* She satirically pledged to never share useful information but keep repeating the mantra our combined art force will never be enough unless used to pull apart and push apart. Since my divorce, I've vowed to never forget I lack the courage to care so I must project useless fear.' She stared sardonically momentarily then threw her chair.

Sade, the graphic designer said, 'Ladies, I agree with Margaret, we have seeds to sow and need space to grow, lest we forget *a room of one's own* to practice intellectually and spiritually. Our gardens do need tending year-round, so to speak. Why don't we throw out the scorebook, graphs and charts, stop making predictions, outlining pitfalls, and heal this cash-counting addiction? I'm not saying I want you to want what I want; I'm saying I want us to each hear what we want. Not because the getting's good but because it feeds the greater good. There's no need to set things in stone, just set things in motion out of devotion to ourselves and for our children.'

The women cheered but a new leader commandeered, appearing out of nowhere appropriating, 'The same situation juxtaposed but grounded a little closer to home, no offence, Sade. We're trending now so let others follow but follow in return and let reciprocity burn the books of elitism, hedonism and chauvinism in all its forms.'

A hairpin fell out of Zola's hair.

'Grace and Zola, are you still here? Don't get me wrong . . . ' the self-appointed leader continued, ' . . . Sade's song is in key just off point as Hastings is no longer stained with urban decay. The blight's an opportunity for us now to be anything we want to be.' She laughed uncontrollably then went in for the kill. 'We'll boycott the coffee shops with seats for customers only. We'll show them, they'll see. We'll ask the council where all the public benches have gone. We'll make a video about their role in this town. I'll write the script and call it *The Death of the Arcades will be the Death of Me.*

A little-known fact; I lived here as a child and got picked on for being fat. On the beach they'd call me darky even though I've got no African in me. Thank God I don't shop at the supermarket and instead opt to grow things in my garden, which by the way you can steal at a bargain at tomorrow's market. I'm a trooper, not an enterpriser, a true artist and I'm surprised some don't see this, but I expect it's cultural bias.'

Now lastly and very quickly; 'Sade, are you having trouble sleeping of late? The poor girl in the chemist shouldn't have said. She also mentioned vacating her home; evicted and relocated by that gay housing officer you're dating. I only bring it up because it left a good family homeless and what with no money it got pretty ugly as I'm sure you'll agree. Thank God I do loans at Barclays; ever the shepherd I let the burden fall on me. Now, regarding our logo, sorry Sade, it's a no-go. My husband's firm will do it for cheap.'

Meeting adjourned.

Spooling a Spinning Reel

Adrian Self

But the Quincunx of Heaven runs low, and 'tis time to close the five ports of knowledge. We are unwilling to spin out our awaking thoughts into the phantasms of sleep, which often continueth precogitations; making Cables of Cobwebs and Wildernesses of handsome Groves.

- From *The Garden of Cyrus* by Sir Thomas Browne

In July 2012, supported by a small grant from The Institute for Sonic History and The English Nature Department for Eco-Acoustics, I set off to walk and record in and around the seaside town of Hastings, in the hope of capturing the echoes of time past and passing, and to remedy a personal malady; a dissociative disorder relating to natural phenomena, from which I had suffered for many years.

Setting out from high above The Old Town, aiming to reach The Bohemia Walled Garden before the end of the day, I was flooded with invigorating feelings of excitement and despair. My mind cocooned from the world in padded headphones, I descended the Harold Road, recording the sound of children playing in the compact green rectangle of an infant school playground, mixed with gentle birdsong, the wind blowing through the trees and the grinding rumble and whoosh of a thousand distant combustion engines. In front of an abandoned house sat a most curious array of former carousel animals; a lobster, a zebra and a lioness, brightly coloured fibreglass creatures, their whirling days long departed. The sound of the grass growing abundantly around them was, I almost believed, audible through my omnidirectional microphones.

I stumbled; the footpath had narrowed to a sharp point as it approached the junction with Barley Lane, enclosing me in a tiny triangle and I was forced to cross the road, entering involuntarily the northernmost tip of the Old Town's High Street. I felt an awkward vertigo: had I suddenly grown to gigantic proportions or was it the shrunken size of the buildings? Only the familiar shape of cars reassured me I had not unexpectedly expanded like Alice. The cause of my disturbance was most definitely rooted in the designs of the external world. I felt foolish, recalling reading about these miniaturised dwellings in a 1976 Sight and Sound interview with German film director Werner Herzog. Raised up on a bank from the sloping street stands a miniature country house, without a number, once owned and occupied by Helmut Döring, one of the stars of Herzog's 1970 drama *Even Dwarves Started Small*, a film in which a group of dwarves take over an unspecified institution, setting fire to flower pots, laughing as a camel struggles to its feet, murdering a capuchin monkey and setting a small truck to spin driverless in an infinite, meaningless circle. According to Herzog, Döring had heard about the Old Town's small houses and imagined they had been developed as an 18th Century separatist community inhabited solely by those born with dwarfism, and his own house, Döring fancied, was orignally inhabited by the town's only notary. The Hastings of 1976, when Döring lived at the house hoping to re-establish such a community, was not a happy time for German dwarves and the film star (though few people locally had seen his film) suffered at the hands of local residents. According to Herzog, Döring left the town on the night of Saturday July 3rd 1976 after having seen The Sex Pistols perform as support act to the Welsh heavy metal band Budgie in a gig on Hastings Pier, leaving with the punk group in their van and travelling back to London where he briefly joined the entourage that surrounded the English filmmaker Derek Jarman. The two would ultimately come to blows during preparation for Jarman's Dungeness film *The Garden*. Budgie, the rock group from Cardiff, now all but forgotten, were promoting their album *If I Were Britannia I'd Waive The Rules*. The cover featured a small flock of budgies wearing astronaut suits, flying above the searchlights of a war metropolis; the band wasted no opportunity in celebrating the title of their album from the Pier stage raised, as it was, just a few hundred feet above the crashing waves of the English Channel.

I continued to walk down the High Street. I recorded, with pleasing clarity, the sound of dog excrement being scooped into a plastic bag by a diligent septuagenarian couple fussing around a small Yorkshire terrier. It called to mind another person who had experienced an epiphany, as so many would later claim to have done during early performances by that band encapsulated in the beatific sneer of Johnny Rotten; Marianne Joan Elliott-Said was in attendance that night. It was her 19th birthday. With a white mother and Somalian father, Marianne had also suffered from the intolerance of the townsfolk and was determined to escape. As she said in an interview, *I lived on what we foraged in the forest. I did a lot of walking through the night, hitch-hiked from one free festival to the next, stayed in hippie crashpads. I walked in a stream in north Devon all the way to the sea. I sat on a rock with a guy who looked like he was from another planet, with long, platinum-blond hair, blue robes, white eyebrows.* Marianne's adventures came to an end after wading bare foot through one too many rivers and, having trodden on a rusty nail, she contracted septicemia and was forced to return to Hastings. Following the concert on the pier she re-emerged as Poly Styrene, singer of X-Ray Spex whose songs include the liberationist anthem 'Oh Bondage Up Yours!' and the anti-consumerist 'Plastic Bag'. The smell of dog excrement and thoughts of Marianne's septicemia caused a profound nausea to descend upon me.

I took shelter in The Old Town Museum; in the museum's shop I was pleasantly reminded of the root of the word vaccine from the latin for cow (vaccae) by a small pamphlet detailing *The History of Smallpox in Sussex* that I purchased for 40p. A Hasting's farmer named Tester observed how his milkmaids were immune to the disease and had exposed his wife and five young children to cowpox in the hope of similarly protecting them from its more dangerous relation. This was the first recorded case of deliberate vaccination; Tester was fined and sentenced to stand in the pillory for an undisclosed period of time.

Recovering, resting on a red velvet chair and removing my headphones, I read one of the many information boards that divided the museum's internal space. The storms that ravaged the town, countless natural disasters, the silting of the harbour, cliffs crumbling into the sea since 9500 BC when the ice age retreated sufficiently for early Europeans to advance and hunt for woolly rhino and reindeer before being marooned, once the waters had risen high enough for this land to be separated from the continent, some 3500 years later.

An unidentifiable taste in my mouth, I replaced the headphones over my ears and retreated to the street, continuing my descent to the sea. Bright low sunlight hurt my eyes. I raised my hand as a shield and stumbled across The Bourne, past the gaudy shell statue on Winkle Island, commemorating the Hasting's fishermen's Winkle Club, a charitable organisation supporting the underprivileged. The silver statue's surface reflected the hard grey tiling of the Jerwood Gallery across the street. I could see in the curved mirrored surface a languid gull, standing motionless on the roof of a truck that was delivering food and drink for the gallery's cafeteria. I read later on the galley's website that the cafeteria shows a strong commitment to quality, sustainable fishing and food; *we have designed a fantastic bespoke menu for the Gallery, which makes the best of local produce, yet is affordable.* The gull eyed me unwaveringly as I recorded its occasional shrieks.

Behind the Jerwood I saw the extended black wooden sheds of The Stade's famous net shops and I walked in their shadow as if in a dream, the distant memory of a childhood fear; the slipping away from the protective fingers of a parent to drift within the darkness surrounding the stern ambiguous giants, tightlipped and unwilling, or unable, to reveal their intent. I stumbled through the stone doorway of what I believed to be a church, but upon further inspection, turned out to be another museum, only 200 metres from the last. The Hastings Fishermen's Museum. Inside the shell of the former chapel stood an enormous dark wooden fishing boat. It resembled the pulpit fashioned as the prow of a whaling vessel, graced by the stout figure of Orson Welles performing as Father Mapple in the 1956 adaptation of *Moby Dick*. Confused, I heard Welles' booming voice preaching the story of Jonah through the conduit of my recording equipment, *The sea vomited out Jonah upon the dry land, his ears like two seashells still multitudinously murmuring of the ocean.*

I wandered around the museum's display of fishing history. The ships and crews that had been lost were many, the storms and fires that waged relentless war upon the fishermen graphically described. The most curious exhibit was a diorama of the shingle beach, with scale models of the tall dark net shops and at its heart the exterior of the museum itself, in which I was currently standing simultaneously looking both from the inside and out, feeling a strange disequilibrium. The huge belly of a German U-boat, dismantled and stripped for its iron, took up a generous portion of the wall of a small annex; the submarine was stranded on the beach on 15th April 1919, recorded in a local paper, the boat appearing a helpless yet sinister monster as it rolled in the surf only a few yards from the promenade. The vessel was displayed to the public before being recycled for its metal skin. A small clipping behind glass described how the two coastguards who had showed visitors around while the boat lolled on the shingle died within nine months of its final destruction. Cause of death, inhalation of noxious substances, expelled from the sub's inner workings.

I too was unable to breath freely, surrounded by the stifling flotsam of history. I paused briefly to purchase a sepia-toned postcard from 1909 of a working horse, plodding a long slow circular path around a wooden capstan, to winch up another fishing boat onto the beach in the last days of sail. I stepped out into the white sun and crunched across the stones, to sit and rest, to record the sound of waves striking the sea wall and the constant wind that caused the brown rusted railings surrounding the car park to whine a mournful tune. My back to the land, I rested on my hands and enjoyed the amplified cacophony within the swaddling of my headphones. When I attempted to rise, my wrists and hands were numb, floppy and awkward, the flippers of a seal, unsuited for movement out of the water. I shook them in front of me like windmills to reflow the blood and walked up to the East Hill Lift, the funicular railway that rises above Rock-a-Nore Road to take visitors to Hastings Country Park and its Sites of Special Scientific Interest. These include cliff top acid grassland, ancient wooded gill streams and an array of rare and vulnerable species. The lift, as I had known for many years, was originally powered by a water balance system – both stations have a tank and a pump and with the effect of gravity, the displacement of liquid lifts the carriage to the summit. From 1888 to 1933 this system was powered by the first waste refuse incinerator in the country. The metallic machinations of the pulleys and cranks sounded different today, attached as they now were to the National Grid. From the bottom of the cliff I walked to Flamingo Park to record the laughter and screams of the amusement park; but it was a Wednesday afternoon during the academic year. Despite the sunshine, the dodgems, merry-go-rounds and go-karts were deserted, spinning and rolling emptily to the digital clatter and flashing neon of slot machines. Abandoned rides were fashioned into fire engines, transit vehicles, space shuttles, the Cookie Monster and Hello Kitty. At the edge of Flamingo Park I captured the sound of swan pedaloes bobbing and knocking in the gentle ripples of a boating lake. A vague recollection came to mind of a local newspaper report, a number of years before, in which two local schoolboys had truanted from school, lifted one of the swans to the Channel and had unsuccessfully attempted to escape to France.

After a few minutes of recording the traffic gyrating through a roundabout, its centre an ornate water fountain obscured from passersby by a concrete safety wall, I entered the retail centre of Hastings through a dark pedestrian subway, walking past the John Logie Baird public house which commemorates the inventor who created the first working television set from a combination of an old hatbox, a pair of scissors, needles, a few bicycle lights, sealing wax, glue and a rotating disc of round holes in a site close by. I attempted to enter the Debenhams department store but the automatic door refused to respond to my approach. Beside the closed door, a blue plaque informed that Beatrix Potter wrote two stories in a house at 16 Robertson Terrace on the site of the store, during a rainy holiday she had taken in 1903, *The Tale of 2 Bad Mice* and *The Pie and the Patty*, a story about a cat who reluctantly invites a dog to attend a tea party ('A little dog, indeed! Just as if there were no CATS') that explores the spiral of behaviour brought about by the mutability of polite social mores. I turned 180 degrees and walked towards the sea. I could see two steep roads descending to meet at an antapex with a dark tunnel. I had recently seen a film about long-term storage of spent radioactive nuclear fuel and how best to protect future generations that may no longer understand current forms of human communication, who might blunder innocently upon buried poisonous waste. As I drew nearer to the tunnel, I began to record the hollow echoes of sound emanating from the darkness. I shivered, perceiving the sounds of a future apocalypse, until a Nissan Micra appeared from the gloom. The site was the entrance to an underground car park.

Continuing in a westerly direction, I documented the sounds of activity from the Lost Souls tattoo parlour, Trinity Wholefoods, the Café des Arts and Collared, a dog accessory and gift shop; behind the shop's grand façade I noted the array of canine clothing before being drawn to a Talking Telescope, stationed by the promenade railings overlooking the beach.

For extended viewing insert additional money now or at any time during the view period. Viewing starts after 3 bleeps. Bleep. Bleep. Bleep. Welcome to Hastings.

Hastings was one of the five original Cinque Ports established by Royal Charter in 1155 to maintain ships ready for the Crown in case of need. In return the towns were exempt from tax and tallage, had the right of soc and sac, tol and team, blodwit and fledwit, pillory and tumbril, infangentheof and outfangentheof, mundbryce, waifs and strays, flotsam and jetsam and ligan. Hastings Pier was designed by Eugenius Birch. It was opened on Monday 5th August in 1872. In 1917 the original Oriental Style Pavilion was destroyed by fire, during the Second World War the pier head was sectioned to prevent possible use by German invasion. It suffered bomb damage and reopened in 1946. The pier is currently closed, structural problems caused by erosion and arson attacks. Looking out to sea a person may be lucky enough to spot bottle-nosed dolphin, harbour porpoise and the common and grey seals that sometimes frequent these waters.

Each Talking Telescope in Hastings provides a different commentary. The sky blacked out as the telescope's timed shutter closed. I was convinced I had captured, in the background, the sounds of the Battle of the Somme in 1916. Many, at the time, claimed it could be heard from this beach. I remembered a photograph of the single bomb that was dropped by a Zeppelin into the sea in 1914, causing a bright phospherescence from either the flash of the explosive or the enhanced glow of the herring feeding on phytoplankton at the water's surface.

I ambled on to the base of Bohemia Road and looked up to the hills above and the greenery of White Rock Gardens, where I knew a model village and crazy golf course once stood. There are the remnants of the site of a floral clock with wheels within wheels of carefully manicured pansies, petunias and hollyhocks. This once commemorated William Willet, inventor of British Summer Time, who tirelessly campaigned, in a pamphlet of the same name, for an end to *The Waste of Daylight*.

On Monday December 2nd 1935, twenty years after Willet's death, Grey Owl (Washaquonasin), the Native American pioneer of conservation made an appearance at The White Rock Theatre presenting *Pilgrims of the Wild*, an illustrated talk about his work as caretaker of park animals at Riding Mountain National Park in Manitoba. *You are tired with years of civilization. I come to offer you – what? A single green leaf.* Mary McCormick a local resident was recorded saying to a friend, *That's Archie Belaney, or I'll eat my hat.* I listened through my headphones for the reverberations of the talk and the damning revelation above the sounds of the traffic. The famous Grey Owl was a native of Hastings, having been born and raised in the town by two impoverished maiden aunts. Belaney, a grammar school boy known for an obsession with cowboy stories and a habit of keeping a menagerie of local wildlife in his bedroom collected on illicit nighttime excursions, had temporarily escaped the town and had reinvented himself as a mixed race Native American. Having read from the book of nature revealed to him by his Indian wife, he returned to evangelize for its protection. The cars, buses, trucks and caravans that filled my ears increased my anxiety. This fake shaman, did he tell his lies to impart a greater truth? Or in the words of his publisher Lovat Dickson, *We had been duped*? There was no Arcadia. Machines were our masters, and we had been deluding ourselves in thinking that we could defy them. I flinched as a high-pitched tone filled my ears, a warning my batteries were running low.

I turned once more to the sea.

I once heard a story, a legend: the only way to permanently

break the grip of Hastings, and to avoid an endless but inevitable return to the town, was to take with you a rock hewn from the castle walls before you attempt to leave.

I observed the rusty iron framework, wooden spikes, scaffolding and security fencing on the promenade around the abandoned pier pointing disconsolately to the horizon, the sign 'You Can Save Me!' and the computer generated architectural plans for future regeneration. 3D walkthroughs of glass and steel cinemas, restaurants and retail units. Out to sea an extraordinary craft appeared, constructed from collapsed wooden sheds, glasshouses and driftwood by some Robinson escaping his island; it sailed slowly and awkwardly, frequently caught in the eddies and whirlpools close to the shore in search of new land. In the last few moments of power retained by my equipment I attempted to capture its sound.

....

Notes

1 *All the recordings described will be available for download with the digital coversion of this report.*

2 *I didn't ever find the Bohemia Walled Garden.*

I'm Gonna Move to Hastings

Salena Godden

'I'm Gonna Move to Hastings' first appeared in Under the Pier
(Nasty Little Press, 2011)

I'm gonna move to Hastings
pick up where I left off
I'm gonna get drunk every day
with drunks who piss me off
I'm gonna move to Hastings
become the fancy blow job queen
get a job in a dirty dark pub
with a broken ice machine

I'm gonna move to Hastings
where it's two quid for triple house gin
I'll go mental, crazy eyed
wear no shoes and go through bins
I'm gonna move to Hastings
sleep with bouncers and not the bands
in the toilets I have fishermen finger me
with tattooed, corn rough hands

I'm gonna move to Hastings
spend my benefits on the booze
get off with people's boyfriends
get in cat fights which I'll lose
I'm gonna move to Hastings
smoke cheap fags and score shit gear
get bloated on chips and vodka
have weird sex beneath the pier

I'm gonna move to Hastings
teenage mothers pissing on the street
white stilletoes without irony
blistering on their feet
I'm gonna move to Hastings
where it's as cheap as chips
and the bad boys, they crack on
even when the condom rips

I'm gonna move to Hastings
go as low as high can go
we all suck on Hastings rock
it's the hardest rock I know
I'm gonna move to Hastings
bed-sit with a vague view of the sea
sign on the sick, save my medication
burn these poems, when they burn me.

On Hastings Prom

Madeleine McDonald

We have the photo somewhere still
Among the boxed-up jumble of our life

Four old ladies
Sitting on a bench
On Hastings prom
Gaily singing carols
To the blue-grey sea

Graciously
They allowed us to take their picture
We're on honeymoon
We chorused in return

That Christmas the weather was kindly
Hastings showed us a welcoming face
We dreamed of buying a house
High on the hill

One year later we returned
Noticing this time the pinched faces
And dejected figures clutching plastic bags
Bits of shopping – or the detritus of sad lives?

Dreams are fragile
Dissolving on contact with reality
Dreams are resilient
Reborn in the most unlikely places

We never bought that house
But we have photographs
And our memories
Hastings – shabby, careworn, rain-soaked Hastings
Is our home from home

Ordinary magic transforms ordinary lives
How to open people's eyes
How to make them stop and listen
To old ladies singing on a bench?

The Beirut of a Hastings Saturday Night

Salena Godden

Excerpt cut from an early first draft of Springfield Road *written in Hastings in 2006 and edited for this anthology in 2013.*

Our walk begins at Hastings Pier.

It's about 1987 and I promised I'd meet you here, this very Saturday. It's lunchtime and a crisp, bright day, fresh and hopeful; this is the first weekend of the school Easter holidays.

I have clipped my hair up, the sea breeze mushes it up, it's not quite right. I nervously finger spit and twizzle the frizzy, wet-look gel'd strands by my temples and ears. My young mouth is gleeful with lip-gloss the sticky flavour of bubblegum. There you are by the traffic lights outside the White Rock Theatre. I wave at you, you cross the road and we say hello. I'm excited to see you. I talk too fast, come this way, I say hooking my arm into your arm as we walk onto the pier, colourful and noisy with electronic voices and pop music. We can smell an assortment of burnt sugar and grease, doughnuts and chips. We change a one pound note into copper coins to play the old penny machines

Later stepping outside onto the boardwalk, you smile and produce a most exotic purple cigarette, you tell me its a Sobrane. You have ripped off a piece of a matchbox, you have a pocket of loose matches. You try to strike the match but the cardboard keeps flopping, you strike a match on the side of the wall and then on a dry plank. Finally alight and its then you tell me you stole five cigarettes from your Mum's handbag. You show me your hand, it's a rainbow of fags. When we smoke we inhale with intent and look serious to look cool, we make a point not to cough. We agree we both like the colour purple and *The Color Purple* and Prince's film *Purple Rain* and we nod knowing we know all the words.

Looking over the railings, the sea below is a watery broth, a soup of murky green greul. Fishermen huddle in the nooks and crannies, casting lines into the swirls below. They let us know we are intruding, trespassing on their peace and quiet. A briny old fishing-man in a woolly hat, tuts at us and shakes his head, you give him the finger and I grab your hand away and we run away laughing, cheeks all flushed, eyes glittering with mischief.

Leaving the pier, we take a right, and head west along the seafront, towards the Old Town. We pass the Crazy Golf and the Go-Carts and there on the other side of the road I point out the old Bingo hall and arcades. If we listen we'll hear traffic lights, gulls, a distant car radio plays Frankie Goes to Hollywood 'Relax' whilst Chaka Khan's 'I Feel For You' is a constant, booming out of the parade of amusement arcades.

Along the front pensioners with blue-rinse perms and flasks of tea, stare ahead in stoney silence, nodding into space and the horizon. Meanwhile bleach-haired kids, tipex-thinner-suckers, bong-heads, gothic self-harmers, slug from plastic bottles of farmers shit-the-bed-cider. They will meet under the pier, smoke, stare into exactly the same stoney silence, nodding into space and the horizon.

There are Easter holiday day-trippers taking the sea air. They eat sandwiches, sit on the cold pebbles with a wind-break. They actually pay for a deck chair and a new bucket and spade. They stay for the weekend at the caravan-holiday-park, you feel sorry for them, traipsing belligerently behind their parent, slouching, sucking on lurid-coloured slush-puppies.

There are foreign-language students in pastel pringle sweaters and casual cotton Farrah trousers. You can always spot the brand new language students, they huddle and walk like ducklings in twos, dorky matching t-shirt and colour co-ordinated rucksacks. You know robbing them is as easy as shooting fish in a barrel. Boys are like the gulls, but working in gangs, distracting them to steal their walkmans and back packs. Local Hastings girls play the longer game, they let the students buy them chips or a coke, then they'll kiss them later when its dark. Seaside holiday romances last as long as an ice-cream queue, bumper car, puppy love that blossoms with summertimes and always ends with someone saying those five magic words: *I promise I will write.*

Along the front the Regency buildings are battered and weathered, in dire need of a new lick of paint. Hastings needs a holiday from itself. The ice-skating rink and lido are boarded up and closed down. One summer we found a way to sneak into the lido. It was dangerous, the water seemed bottomless, absinthe-cloudy, the tiles were all mildewed and the high diving board was missing a few steps. They say the lido is haunted. I tell you Hastings is haunted, its cursed by Aleister Crowley, you can tell me to shut up, you call me a goff and I laugh.

Ducking down the narrow cobbled back street into the heart of the old town, the arteries are winding alleyways, preserved in salt and a tradition of fishing and smuggling. Walking though the Old Town we pass the tattoo parlour, afternoon tea shops, junk shops, the fish market, selling eels, crabs, cockles and muscles, the candy floss stalls, candied sea shells, shiny windmills, kiss-me-quick hats, buckets and spades. I'll show you the stone sculpture of Winkle Island – that name always makes me smile – I laugh and repeat the name again and again, Winkle Island. But, there, now that's a lovely pub! I'm pointing to the Nelly, a lively fisherman boozer, thick with cigarette smoke, dogs and kids, bikers and pirates. I fight my way to the bar and buy two half pints of cider. I'm quite rich this spring, seeing as I've got two jobs. I tell you, I wash up in a chippy and I also do shifts working in the kitchen of an old people's home too.

The landlady has a heart of gold, she knows we are barely sixteen and too young to get served, but its alright, she'll turn a blind eye, so long as we keep our heads down. Lovely sunny lunchtime so we sit at a table outside The Nelson, there is a dog wanting petting and gulls above. Hear the gulls screaming and above all that the loud jukebox kicking out wailing blues and guitar solos by Neil Young, J.J Cale, John Lee Hooker and John Martyn. John Martyn used to drink here, his song 'Over The Hill' is about that hill, the West Hill, we nod knowing this, our lips know the words. On another table opposite the big bad boys are red-eyed and downing pints. If the tide's right they'll have been in here since dawn. Or is that if the tide's wrong? I forget. But we watch brackish, hard-nut fishermen with blistered rope-burned hands, sloshing beer.

You and me, we suck on a skinny one-skin we blagged to share. Sometimes I roll joints for the fishermen when they are too pissed to see, to lick a rizla. We are quite stoned now, again. It's a lovelylovelylovely haha haha haha ha lovelylovely ha ha . . . Then what happens to the time? We walk and spend the rest of the afternoon in a haze, maybe we'll take a bottle of booze up the cliffs. We'll tell each other massive secrets and stagger through the Old Town, trying to get served in tiny smoky pubs, with low ceilings.

It's early dusk and fuck, how stoned and pissed are we now? And how bloody delicous is the heat wafting from the best chippy in town, the vinegar is carried in the wind, dancing into our nostrils and down into our cidery bellys. We scoff our chips. Our lips are salted, vinegar blue and greasy. We burp, we are dehydrated and sweet headed. And while we are so toasted, we go out the back of The Pig and start playing the longest game of pool. We potted the black hours ago it seems, and now balls roll idly, missing the purpose of pockets.

Meanwhile out there, down on the beach, fresh fish is fetched up the beach in nets, a knot of crabs in cages are dragged up from the boats. There's the frenzied scream of hungry gulls above. And we say what we all say, that thing that someone else once said, what they all always say, Hastings is a lovely little drinking town with a bit of a fishing problem.

This town is littered with people running away from something or running somewhere. Some make new beginnings, start young families. There has always been the refugees and asylum seekers. Hastings is a beehive of Bohemia, of daydreamers and cloud-mongerers, writers and painters, jazz dudes and blues crazies, ageing hippies and war veterans, creatives and eccentrics, witches and new-age healers, the recovering and the convalescents, the winners and the losers, the lovers and the fighters. And the apathetic – Hastings is the birthplace of television.

Down in the belly of the beast, in Hastings town centre it is now Saturday evening and another week is done. The locals and holiday makers collide to drink hard. They are rampant dogs, the hairs on their backs stand up on end. There is a cackling hubbub of excitable girls, dressed in lyrcra, they are skin tone colourful in tangerine, shrimp and salmon pink. With the clip-clop of cheap shoes, as a wonderbra army they march. The girl at the front has a plaster hanging off the back of her heel where the white stilletoes blister. There is the passing note of pot hanging in the air, mixed with the musky acidic-peach of cheap perfume and the sharp tang of sea salt and dead fish.

Cheap music is booming out of cheap nightclubs. They offer two shots for the price of one, there's a good chance of having a bit of a go on it by the bins, fumbling sex, under the pier, blowjobs in the shadows of the beach, a clumsy fuck in the McDonalds side doorway, all for a special price, anything goes on ladies' night. Its Saturday night and it's violent, there is a promise of drama, the antipication of that tat-tat-tat of bullet heels in hot pursuit, the screech of *bitchhhhhh*. The cud-chewing teenage-mothers with their raven-like caw-caw which works in essence as a mating call to the barking mad-dogs drooling in their best-button-down collar shirts. It's a collision of tribes, a war-cry of cackling shrieks, a scream of kebab-breathed laughter, a smashing window, a grinding of glass into the flesh of faces. The smattering of a handbag, as it gushes its contents of lipstick, condoms and bottle of Martini across the pavement on impact. The chundering splat of vomit. The slash and grab, the willful stream of piss, the car alarms and sirens, as dustbins are lobbed, rubbish is strewn, drawing in the police vans and ambulances, a dank stench of small town mentality and boredom.

Then the sour closing-time sing-song chorus of *you slag!* and *do you want some?* and the classic verses of *Leave it, leave it, it's not worth it, just leave it.*

And the same miserable faces every weekend in the taxi queue at the end of the night. There's the podgy girl trembling in her mini skirt, her obligatory goosepimpled bruised-blue legs, never wearing tights, not even in mid-winter. And him with the tattoo on his face, he's just wearing a T-Shirt and a sneer. They neither shiver nor hold each other. They bicker and swear and suck fags. It's not their fault. Bitterly they argue by the puddle of vomit outside the take-away, pieces of kebab meat are like little scraps and nasty starts that don't ever get concluded. The shish kebab is just picked at scabs and murmurs of discontent.

Outside The Crypt, another Saturday night casualty sits crying in the doorway, with two teminations and another on the way. Holding her broken shoe heel, black mascara washes her face, she weeps into the bottle she is nursing. She cries for him with his bloodied nose and all night she's cried for the gear the pigs found in the search. She'll suck her broken lip until next time, when it's just the same, when they are just like last time next time, and always will be, just like every time.

But that's in the town centre, you and me, we sit on the beach and smoke a joint with some friends. The night time sea is all sparkling ink, we look up to name the stars, and the Beirut of a Hastings Saturday night is beautiful and shiny. There in the distance the West and East Hills rise like two plump mounds. The castle is lit up at night with orangey-gold. Hastings castle is an elephants' graveyard nowadays, it eroded and got broken from all the fights and all that weather. The remnants wave a flag of surrender above the chalky, jagged cliffs. Tomorrow, we promise we'll walk to Fairlight and the Firehills. From up there we'll be able to look down at the town with its twitching curtains and small-town lives hung out like dirty knickers on the line and it will be captivating and mundane, at once, nothing and everything.

Below we'll see the rocks are where we went climbing, playing hide and seek as children. Where we'd make camps and play war. I remember us – we were the bare-foot naked summer children. We scooped rivers, irrigated moats around pebbled torrents of wet mud-castles. We jumped from rock to rock with jellied shoes and nets paddling in shallow crab pools.

But now we are big, we are more wary of the cliffs. Its best not go up there alone, for the land might crumble, you may wish it to, you might make it happen that way. You could easily just let go and fall into the swirling sea below, the endless grey-green. When you grow up by the water you cannot help but feel its pull, its power and danger, often you have pictured yourself falling, struggling in rip-tide, drowning, getting smashed and ripped to shreds on the wicked hidden rocks, slippery with moss and as black as beetles' backs.

Right now though, it's you and me, above us a wide and hollow sky, all the sky you could possibly desire, all the sky you could fit into your eyes at once. *Look, if you find a pebble with a hole in the middle you will always return to Hastings,* I give it to you because I love you and I love here and now. Hastings is shabby and beautiful, and you and me, we have no idea what London is . . . We don't even know that next summer they'll invent ecstasy, we'll go to Brighton, we'll go to illegal raves, we'll go to the big city. We have no idea how beautiful and bright we shine. We lie back on the cold pebbles looking for shooting stars, making wishes on satellites, for now this is home and this is Hastings.

V

Into Sussex

Entreprise Bêtise

Rowena Macdonald

'Something's going on out there, Nads.'

'Don't call me Nads.'

'Something's definitely going on. Come and have a look.' Liam was pressed against the window of La Baguette, peering down the rainy high street where nothing ever went on and never had.

'What the – '

'Who the fuck are they?'

Other customers crowded behind Liam. Nadine squeezed between them. Beyond the misted glass were twenty or so people with blue-painted faces pushing a wonky carnival float with a four-piece band on top. The band was playing a tune reminiscent of a children's TV theme that Nadine couldn't quite place. From this distance none of the people were distinguishable beneath their make-up but Nadine knew they weren't from Newhaven.

'Where you going?' shouted Liam as she shoved through the door.

'To have a look.'

'It's raining.'

'So? I'm not made of sugar.'

The performers wore old, torn suits, like the kind that clogged the rails of the local charity shops, the charity shops that outnumbered the real ones. Squeezed between the singer and the guitarist was an old fashioned tripod camera with someone hidden beneath the hood.

Nadine thought she heard the singer shout, 'We have come to bring art to Newhaven,' although it could have been 'heart' because she was dropping and adding aitches all over the place, worse than someone actually from Newhaven. Nadine realised she was French. They were all French.

'We have come to bring art . . . the joy of art . . . the beauty of art . . . ' The troupe handed out flyers to the audience, which was growing despite the rain. Charmaine Dunkley, who had left Tideway the same time as Nadine, was slouched in the entrance of Roy's Liquor Store, sucking on her lip stud, her whiplash eyebrows knotted. Last Nadine heard she had a tag around her ankle for fighting. Kyle, Liam's mate, was on tip-toes trying to see what was happening. A couple of younger kids were balancing on the bin outside I Like 'a' Pizza, taking pictures. Liam's suspicious frown stopped Nadine getting out her own phone.

'Anybody fancy a nice sausage with their art?' shouted the meat-van man parked outside Ladbrokes. 'Six pound a pound. Local pork, hand-reared, hand-made sausages. Work of art, these sausages.'

A bloke outside the White Hart raised his pint: 'Who needs art when you've got beer?'

Someone else shouted, 'Who needs art when you've got fags?'

'Who needs art when you've got drugs?'

'Art is a drug. We will make you addicts to the drug of art.'

'Drugs are a drug.'

'Art, drugs, fags, sausages . . . ' The music adjusted to the chant and the troupe started clapping, encouraging the crowd to join in. ' . . . art, drugs, fags, sausages . . . '

Nadine kept her hands in her pockets.

The person behind the camera emerged from the hood with a flourish. Another blue-painted man, but even through his make-up, Nadine could see he was really good-looking, with lovely lips and cheekbones and a jawline like Robert Pattinson. His dark eyes smouldered in his blue face. French eyes. The bloke from Dieppe who ran the market stall that sometimes came to Newhaven had the same eyes. She once bought a heart-shaped cheese from him because he told her she was *belle*. It cost five pounds and smelled like cow shit. She gave it to Liam, pretended she was being romantic, but they both agreed it tasted like cow shit too so they chucked it away, half a heart, half-eaten. Still, the way the bloke gazed at her with his French eyes . . .

The cameraman's eyes locked onto Nadine. She flicked her gaze away, then back. The man winked, disappeared beneath the hood and the camera flashed.

The troupe moved up the high street, the camera flashing, the crowd following. The blokes from the veg van outside the taxi rank juggled potatoes and threw sprouts. The chant became ' . . . art, potatoes, sprouts, sausages . . . ' The troupe tossed the sprouts in the air, caught them in their mouths and swallowed them.

Nadine remained rooted to the spot, though she wanted to follow. She turned to Liam. He took a swipe on his roll-up. 'What a load of bollocks.'

'*Entreprise Bêtise!*' read the flyer in her hand. '*Be a part of the great*

Newhaven carnival extravaganza this summer! Art, drama, music, fun! Volunteers needed.'

*

'Drama' was the word that had leapt out at her. Drama was her best subject, or at least her favourite; at Sussex Downs she had more competition than at Tideway. Though she hadn't told anyone, Nadine wanted to be an actress. Her other two A-levels were English and French; another reason to get involved. 'I need to practise my oral French,' she imagined telling Liam and predicted his crude retort, but better to pretend it was a joke than allow him to suspect an ulterior motive.

She didn't tell anyone at college in case they wanted to volunteer too. But Friday, first lesson was drama and as soon as she walked in Clara Joseph drawled, 'Look who's here: Newhaven's local celebrity.'

Emily Mason held up a newspaper and there she was in the centre of a photograph, below the words:

THE CIRCUS IS COMING TO NEWHAVEN TOWN.

'Page Three girl of the *Sussex Express*,' said Clara.

Nadine snatched the paper and pored over the picture. Liam's face floated above her shoulder, his eyes narrowed at the photographer who was, obviously, Olivier, the hot French guy, because the photo was the one he had taken. The article explained Entreprise Bêtise's plans in a garbled way: she'd already got the low-down, including Olivier's name, from their website and had 'liked' their Facebook page. Disappointingly, Olivier himself was not on Facebook.

'Can I have my mum's paper back?' said Clara, then Miss Kavanagh came in, and, of course, Clara started shouting her mouth off about the extravaganza.

'Yes, I already know about it, Clara,' said Miss Kavanagh. 'I was going to tell you all this morning but you've beaten me to it. Everyone should get involved. It's going to be brilliant and it'll be a great way of boosting your UCAS forms.'

As Miss Kavanagh explained the project in her usual excitable way, Nadine looked around, at the interested faces and the glazed faces and the avid faces of Clara and Emily. No one else in the class was from Newhaven. Miss Kavanagh should shut up, stop telling these posh Lewes kids about her private thing. Nothing ever happened in Newhaven, nothing arty or dramatic or cool, and she was the one who had spent seventeen years growing up in the place they considered a shithole, so they shouldn't be allowed to celebrate it; because that's what Entreprise Bêtise planned to do: celebrate Newhaven. If anyone outside Newhaven joined in they were hypocrites and bullshitters and just out for themselves, the way Dad always said poshos were.

' . . . are you going to get involved, Nadine?' Miss Kavanagh's red lips beamed and her blue eyes widened in the way that, until now, Nadine had found encouraging.

'Maybe.' Nadine looked at her lap.

'You should, Nadine, because I was talking to Etienne, the director, and he said they haven't enough volunteers from Newhaven yet. They want local people to . . . ' Nadine barely heard the rest. Miss Kavanagh had talked to the director; she called him Etienne, just like that, all casual. She'd probably talked to Olivier too. It was so unfair.

The following week Entreprise Bêtise held a meeting in The

Hope with all the supposed 'local' volunteers. 'What you going there for?' Liam demanded. He was going down The Ark as usual.

'Meeting some girls from college.'

'What girls?'

'Clara and Emily.'

'Why don't you meet them down The Ark? No one goes to the Hope.'

'They want to meet there. I'll come down The Ark later.'

The Hope was at the end of the road leading to the West Beach. On a damp February night, the walk was a miserable prospect, although when she got beyond the harbour the haloed lights in the ferry terminal and the calm expanse of the dark sea suddenly made Newhaven seem romantic. Nadine briefly sensed it wasn't as grim as everyone thought, that glimmering in the corner of her eye was something more than poverty and depression. In the future, her hometown might blossom into something better than a dead-zone strangled by a ring-road with a seeping crawl of council houses and run-down industrial estates.

Pushing into the warm bright interior of The Hope, her reflection glanced back from the mirror behind the bar. The damp air was doing its best to ruin her hair but it was still pretty smooth. Mind you, if she hadn't spent so long straightening it, she would have got there earlier and might have ended up nearer Olivier. He was hemmed in by a bunch of people. Clara and Emily were among them, dressed up to the nines in their most arty-yet-slaggy gear. Miss Kavanagh was also there, wearing a shorter skirt than she ever wore at college, a beret that matched her lipstick, and holding her little girl, Maddie, on her lap. Miss Kavanagh was a single mum; favoured pupils sometimes babysat for her.

Etienne was talking about how he was going to transform

Newhaven into a *'une scène, un théâtre* . . . the whole of the town, *toute les rues, tout le monde*...everyone *participer* . . . you, you, you...' He pointed to an unknown volunteer, then Clara and Emily, who slid their eyes sideways in fake modesty, then he made a sweeping gesture: ' . . . *tout le monde sera comédien, artiste* . . . ' The river, the quay and the harbour were going to be *'plein de feu* . . . *une fleuve en feu* . . . all the boats burning . . . ' Nadine wondered how the fishermen would take that, until Miss Kavanagh clarified that he didn't mean boats would actually be burned but, rather, the fishermen would ferry drummers and people with burning torches along the river.

Mincemeat, Liam's boss, would never let a load of 'artistes' onto his trawler unless there was money involved. The other fishermen would probably feel the same. As far as Nadine could make out, no one was getting paid, except Entreprise Bêtise.

Surreptitiously she studied Olivier. In normal clothes, without a blue face, he was unbelievably good-looking: dark, gothy, bikerish – not her usual type – but he reminded her of Johnny Depp. He was probably about Johnny Depp's age. Certainly a lot older than Liam. Liam was good-looking too – Ryan Gosling-esque – but, lately, well, ever since going to college, she'd wondered if he was right for her. He'd already left school when they got together last spring. She'd been flattered that he fancied her – at Tideway he'd been one of the in-crowd, one of the dominating troublemakers. His work gave him muscles and a tan and made his hair even blonder in the summer. He wasn't rolling in money but at least he had a job and he spent a lot on her. They used to have a real laugh together and she did fancy him, sort of, but she was sick of him complaining that she'd gone 'all posh' just because she was getting educated and wasn't on the dole or pregnant like half the girls in Newhaven.

Olivier had smiled at her vaguely when she first came in but hadn't paid her any particular attention since. She wondered if she had imagined their mutual spark, whether she should bother volunteering. She supposed she could get out of it. As she touched her phone into life and opened a new message – *R u coming to ark? Were r u?x* – she was jerked back into The Hope by Miss Kavanagh saying, 'Yes, go on, Nadine, how do you want to get involved?'

'Uh . . . I dunno . . . I mean, er . . . ' She scanned their expectant faces. ' . . . I'll do whatever you want.'

Everyone burst out laughing.

'Like a sheep to *l'abbatoir* . . .' said Etienne, 'No, that's not right; how do you say *'la brebis à l'abbatoir'*?'

'Like a lamb to the slaughter.' Olivier's teeth and eyes flashed as he turned a grin on Nadine, and she buried her chin in her neck and hoped the blush filling her cheeks wasn't obvious.

*

The event, which Entreprise Bêtise decided to call Newhaven Ooze, was scheduled for 14th July; 'Bastille Day,' as Miss Kavanagh pointed out, though Nadine wasn't quite sure what that meant. Between February and July, not much happened, or not much involving Nadine. She heard via Miss Kavanagh that various local busybodies were organising the logistics of turning the town into *un théâtre*.

'Won't there be rehearsals?' said Nadine. 'What part am I going to play?'

'You can either go on one of the boats,' said Miss Kavanagh. 'The Lewes Bonfire Society drummers will be on them. You could join in, banging a drum – or you can follow Entreprise Bêtise – they'll be parading through the town with fireworks and stuff.'

Nadine glanced at Clara and Emily, who had also hung behind after class. 'What are you two gonna do?'

'I thought we were going to *be* the performers,' said Clara. 'I don't want to follow them. The whole town's going to be following them. I want to be one of them.'

'Yeah, that's what I want,' said Emily.

It was what Nadine wanted too, only she'd never say it so blatantly. She nodded and tried to imply with an earnest gaze that she was more deserving.

The curl at either corner of Miss Kavanagh's mouth tightened.

'Well, I've been in touch with Etienne and Olivier and the rest of the guys and I'm sure that'll be fine. They're rehearsing the whole thing the week before so you can get involved then.'

Heat flared in Nadine at the mention of Olivier.

'Can we have Etienne and Olivier's email addresses, so we can find out exactly what we're supposed to be doing?' Clara had her hands on her hips, which were squeezed into denim hot-pants over leopard-print tights.

'Well, I'm supposed to be co-ordinating you three and I can't give out email addresses without their permission but I'll let you know the rehearsal dates when they tell me.' Miss Kavanagh's perpetual smile and ditzy casualness suddenly seemed fake.

*

Liam was surprisingly unbothered about Nadine volunteering but, unsurprisingly, he didn't want to take part himself. He agreed with Mincemeat: 'What's the point if we're not getting paid?'

Her parents were equally dismissive.

'Where they getting the money for this?'

'I don't know. Europe or something.'

'Europe. Bloody typical. The French have taken over the port, they're running down the harbour, and now they want to waste a load of money prancing around the town in fancy dress . . . Why can't they invest that money in some proper jobs?'

'They're different French people from the ones that own the port.'

'Frogs are all the same, Nadine.'

Mum and Dad had known Newhaven in its boom days, back when every bloke in the town had a job on the docks or the railway or at the Parker Pen factory. Dad had been a docker before containerisation did for the place and ships began offloading goods at bigger ports. Now he was a plasterer. At least he had a job, as he never failed to remind them. The day he didn't mention how hard he worked and how knackered he was, was the day they'd have to check his pulse.

Through the rumours circulating around town, Nadine heard Entreprise Bêtise would be billeted at the Harbourside. She worried it wouldn't be posh enough for them. French hotels probably all had flowery balconies and served croissants for breakfast.

Typically, the start of July was the wettest since records began. Nadine was coming out of the station after college, hunched against the rain, when a massive articulated lorry blocked her way. It was turning arthritically into the road that led to the East Quay. She saw its foreign number-plate, the letter F, looked up at the cab with its windscreen wipers thrashing and there was Olivier, at the wheel on the wrong side, frowning into the wing mirror, a cigarette drooping from his lips.

'Olivier!' In her surprise, Nadine forgot to be shy.

He leaned out of the cab. '*Salut!*' Beyond him, on the passenger seat, a little boy bobbed up and down. Olivier gestured: 'My boy: Remi.'

'Hi Remmy.' Nadine waved. So Olivier had a son. Did that mean he had a wife? Because he was about the same age as her brother and looked friendly, Remi made her feel braver. 'Where are you going?'

Olivier pointed down the road with his cigarette.

'I thought you were all staying at the Harbourside?'

His answer was lost in a peal of beeps from waiting cars. He indicated for her to come round the other side of the cab, hop in. With her nose aloft to the tooting horns, she climbed up and squeezed beside Remi. He was dressed in a pair of leather biker trousers that matched the trousers his dad was wearing, although obviously many sizes smaller. On top he was swamped by a ragged t-shirt with a wolf on the front and, like his dad, his hair was longish. Nadine imagined her mother's disgust at Remi's get-up: Jamie was dressed in normal Primark stuff.

Olivier parked the lorry in the yard on the quayside.

'You're going to sleep here?'

Olivier nodded and revealed behind a curtain at the back of the cab a berth tangled with sleeping bags.

'*Nous dormons là.*' Remi laid his hands by his cheek and pretended to snore. '*Mon Papa et moi.*'

Nadine smiled at the berth with a mixture of disappointment yet relief that she probably wouldn't end up cheating on Liam.

Olivier offered her a Gitane. She didn't really smoke but it was sexy to let Olivier light it with a snap of his Zippo – how totally French not to have a shit plastic lighter – and watch his eyes flicker over her mouth as she sucked in the smoke. The rain had abated and they stood in the yard, staring westwards towards the Fort and the lighthouse, while Remi tried to climb the chain-fence that surrounded them.

'Was the journey OK? Did you come on the ferry?' she asked,

when it became clear that Olivier was not going to bother talking.

'Of course I come on the ferry.' He flicked his fag-end into a puddle. His fingertips were engrained with oil, his nails thick and cracked. Rougher hands than a fisherman, rougher than Liam's certainly. She was supposed to meet Liam at The Ark later. He was out at sea now. She considered asking Olivier if he had seen any fishing boats on the crossing, but realised this would sound as lame as her last question. Instead she said, 'Do you know what I'm going to have to wear?'

'I expect we paint you blue all over and make you to wear, how you say . . . *en haillons* . . . '

'En high-on?'

Remi ran up and pressed against his dad; their leather trousers squeaked as they met. Olivier rubbed Remi's tattered t-shirt between his fingers. 'Like this.'

'I have to wear a wolf t-shirt?'

'No! Something old, with many holes.'

'Oh: something ragged. I'll have to wear rags?'

'*Exactement.*' He smiled, his teeth white against his olive skin. '*Comme Cendrillon.*'

'What?'

'The poor girl in the fairy story, with the two ugly sisters, who goes to the ball and becomes the princess.'

'Oh: Cinderella?'

Remi jumped up and down, pointing at the sky. '*Papa, regarde – un arc-en-ciel!*'

A rainbow was arching over the West Quay.

'Ah, lovely.' Nadine sighed. 'You should've called it Newhaven Rainbow not Newhaven Ooze . . . It looks like the pot of gold is exactly where – '

The theme from *Mission Impossible* began pounding from

Olivier's phone. Nadine smiled at Remi, who was staring at the rainbow, and tried to decipher what Olivier was saying. His French was terse, with none of the embarrassing ponciness of her A-level teacher. All she could make out were '*ouis*' and a word that sounded like 'pub'. He snapped the phone shut with the same dashing brusqueness as his Zippo.

'The others, they start drinking already . . . The Ark, do you know it?'

'Uh . . . yes.'

'I am meeting them there. You want to come?'

'Oi, Nadine. What you doing here already?'

Liam's voice grated across the mellifluous French hubbub. He was filthy from the boat, hair spiked with sea salt, work-boots giving him a rangy swagger. Neil, the skipper, lumbered in behind. Nadine was surrounded by Entreprise Bêtise, just about keeping up with her C-grade French. She loved the way they made her name sound so chic and was thrilled they had said she could be at the front of the procession. Olivier was at the bar, buying her another Bacardi and coke. He turned at Liam's entrance.

'This is the theatre lot,' said Nadine. Liam looked blank. 'From *France.*'

'Oh *right.*'

During the kerfuffle of introductions Nadine prayed Liam and Neil wouldn't say the word 'frog'. They didn't and instead basked in the interest in their job, told the French what they had caught, how much they'd get for it. Olivier told Liam he liked fishing himself – 'for fun, *un passe-temps* – I am not *pêcheur de métier*'; they discussed at length the different varieties of fish in the Med and the Channel. Nadine couldn't believe it: her boyfriend found it easier to talk to Olivier than she did. As the evening wore on, she worried Liam would end up getting involved. The French implored him to persuade Mincemeat to volunteer his boat.

'He won't: he's a right tight-arse. He don't see the point.'

'To be honest,' said Neil, 'I know what Mincemeat means. Not being funny, no disrespect or nothing, but it's a lot of effort for one evening; what is the point?'

Etienne made a dismissive kissing expression. 'The point is to get involve in a unique piece of performance art. It's an experience.'

'That's what Nad said, but, honestly, Mincemeat won't get it. Anyway, I'm shit at acting and anything like that. Neil's not exactly Leonardo di Caprio either. You don't want stupid wankers like us. You want good-looking birds like Nadine.' Liam put his arm around Nadine and started going on about how he was 'really proud' of her acting talent, that she was 'the brainiest girlfriend' he'd ever had – 'and not just brainy: really fit too'. He pressed her against him so she was overwhelmed by his fish stink and no one was in any doubt that they were together.

*

'You smell,' said Nadine when they got to her front gate and Liam leaned in for a snog.

'That's not very nice. What's got into you?'

'Nothing.' Nadine bucked her head away from his beer-sour mouth.

'You've had the hump all the way home.'

'No, I haven't. I'm just tired.' She extricated herself from his heavy arms.

'What's the matter? I'm only trying to be nice. I talked to your froggy mates all night, listened to them wank on about their stupid theatre bollocks.'

'I thought you were interested.'

'I was being polite.'

'You're not usually polite.'

'What's that supposed to mean?'

'I don't know.' Nadine didn't even know why she was so angry. 'You might as well go home.'

'Come on . . . Nads . . . '

'Don't fucking call me that.' A light flicked on upstairs. 'Oh bloody hell, now you've woken mum and dad.'

'Oh suit yourself, stuck up cow. See if I fucking care.'

*

Newhaven Ooze burst onto the town in a way that made its title a misnomer. At dusk the narrow shabby streets were filled with people in ragged pirate gear, wielding flaming torches, rolling burning barrels and throwing firecrackers. The River Ouse was crammed with boats of drummers, beating out a rhythm to back up the sinister fairground tune from the band, which was towed on a flat-bed truck disguised as a pirate ship. The dark water glittered with reflected light and clouds of purple and orange smoke rose from the boats as the fishermen set off flares, their booms punctuating the drumbeat. Crowds gathered. The cynicism that had swirled in preceding weeks evaporated. People laughed in the flamelight and gasped at the fireworks and were awed by the handsome pirates swashbuckling through their town. At the front of the procession, in a tattered shirt with frilled cuffs, thigh-high boots and a tri-corn hat was Nadine. No-one recognised her because, like the other pirates, her cheekbones were swiped with Dayglo stripes and her eyes were feline with kohl. For most of the procession she carried a fiery torch and shouted pirate curses in English and French, but at the start of the road leading to the marina, she and the others slit open sacks of goose feathers strung between the fish store and the lamp-posts. They slit them with shiny swords so the purple twilight was filled with feathers as well as fire. Further along they slit sacks of golden chocolate coins that showered across the path and which the crowd stole like treasure. And, by the West Beach, the finale: rockets splashed molten lava into the sky and a pirate ship, marooned on the shore, was torched into a pyre while pirates spun flaming hula hoops and juggled flaming clubs, and Olivier zip-wired from the cliff flailing a cutlass.

Nadine tossed her hat to the ground before lighting the torch. Someone shouted 'Oi, Nadine!' but they were drowned out by the roar of flames. She hadn't seen Liam during the procession; she suspected he'd miss it to spite her. Her parents she'd glimpsed further back, through a flurry of goose feathers but they'd stared at her with the same uncomprehending astonishment as the rest of the crowd. It was so freeing to be someone else. Performing wasn't just about showing off, it was about transforming everything, including yourself, into something more exciting. The past week she'd forgotten about Liam, forgotten about normal life. Every evening after college she had gone down to the warehouse on the North Quay, where Entreprise Bêtise rehearsed the show, and there, she had been given a crash course in eating fire. At first she'd been terrified of setting her hair alight or scarring her face but fear of looking sappy made her reckless. Even Remi could swallow a lit match and, once she'd got over the taste of paraffin and borne the pain of a blistered tongue, she could eat fire as if it was candy floss.

'You're a natural,' Olivier said, when she first managed to place a fire torch in her mouth and, though he'd said the same thing to Clara and Emily, she still glowed. No-one knew who she really was or cared where she was from. They treated her like an adult, like a professional. This was their work and she was part of it. Work didn't have to be a grim struggle, half-killing yourself doing something boring like Liam and Dad. These people had run away to the circus and they made money.

The last firework faded to nothing, the pyre shrank, the flames were extinguished from the hulas and the torches were snuffed out. The show was over and the crowd slunk back to where they had come from.

An after-party had been organised in Meeching Hall by the town council. Clara and Emily and the other volunteers went on ahead. Nadine hung around for Olivier to finish whatever he was doing among the burnt debris. She checked her phone. *Sorry babez. Will u 4give me? I miss u. Kyle having party. Come round when u finished with theatre bollox. xx*

She turned. Olivier was a silhouette against the ebbing fire.

'You go,' he shouted. 'I come later.'

As she walked to Meeching Hall, she decided that later she would ask Olivier whether she could join Entreprise Bêtise. The plan had been brewing in her mind all week. Sod Uni. Mum and Dad couldn't afford the fees anyway.

Harsh electric light flooded out of the open door of the hall. Inside, the English shovelled peanuts into their mouths and sloshed boxed wine into polystyrene cups. The French lounged around the edges of the hall still partially in costume. Clara and Emily had changed into their hot-pants and were gyrating to Rihanna's 'Live Your Life', which grated tinnily from an iPod plugged into a small speaker. Etienne, reclining on a plastic chair with an unlit cigarette in his mouth, smiled indulgently at their crotches. He took out a box of matches and struck one.

'Sorry, mate, can't smoke in here: public place; same laws in France, I'm sure,' said the Mayor of Newhaven, whom Nadine only identified as such because a big medallion was slung over his suit. Etienne shrugged and ambled outside.

In came Olivier with Remi, both dressed in the remnants of their pirate finery. Behind was Miss Kavanagh with her daughter. Remi and Maddie ran to the peanuts and began tossing them into the air and catching them in their mouths. Nadine watched Olivier lead Miss Kavanagh to the wine and put his arm around her. The situation was suddenly strip-light clear. She slipped out as fast as she could and walked without looking back until she was nearly at Kyle's flat. She stopped, peered at her reflection in a car mirror, and wiped away with her frilly cuffs the rivers of mascara running down her fluorescent cheeks.

Kyle's party could be heard from the end of his street. People loitered by the front wall, smoking and drinking. Charmaine Dunkley was among them.

'A-haarr, shiver me timbers,' she snickered. 'Look who it is: Captain Jacqueline Sparrow.'

Nadine turned on her heel. Fuck them all, she was going home. She came face-to-face with Liam, sauntering in with a bag of cans. He stared at her evenly.

'Alright Nadine, have you finally come back down to earth?'

Acknowledgments

The editors would like to thank all of our contributors, our designer Chris Smisson, Nick Santos Pedro our digital director, Travis Elborough, Short Run Press, Gareth Rees, Sam Berkson, Hackney Downs Studios, 3:AM Press, Galley Beggar, Daniel at the Lonely Coot, Structo Magazine, APF, London Radical Bookfair, and the Stoke Newington Literary Festival.

Gary would like to thank Nina Robertson, Kevon Budden, Steve Budden, Lynne Wilson, The Journal of Wild Culture, the *Ambit* team, and the Kent coast.

Kit would like to thank Valerie and Sally Caless, Helen Jacobs, Meghna Gupta, Aditi, Anish and Soma Gupta, Rob Jackson, The Duke crew, The Watkins family for the seaside memories, Ed and Richard at Resonance FM and Femi at NTS. Mostly though, we want to thank that stretch of water that runs from Planet Thanet to dear old Hastings. Without your salty charm, this book would not exist.

Biographical Notes

Aziza Abdullah is a Londoner living in Hastings. Themes regularly explored in her work include delinquency, veganism, mythology, multiculturalism, feminism and Islam.

Iain Aitch is a Margate-born author, journalist and flâneur. He has written two books on British culture and continues his research into the subcultures of the UK. He lives in east London. You can find him at www.iainaitch.com.

Joana Batista is an illustrator with a passion for contemporary art. She has a Visual Arts Master from the University of Camberwell and draws everyday. You can find some of her work in http://littleoakillustration.blogspot.fr/.

Craig John Barr is an artist, illustrator, workshop instructor and the designer, curator and founder of the Salford Zine Library. Craig is based in Manchester, England and graduated with a BA (Hons) in Illustration in 2009 from the University of Central Lancashire. He has been commissioned professionally as an illustrator, curator, printmaker and educator since 2006.

Joe Becci is an illustrator born and living in South-east England, with an undying love for creating interesting characters and fantastical worlds. joe-becci.blogspot.co.uk

Mark Beechill lives and sometimes works in Canterbury, Kent, and blogs at http://lessthanfivehundredpress.blogspot.co.uk & http://monkeyintheruins.blogspot.co.uk. In his spare time, he worries that if he ever gets a job that he actually enjoys, he will have nothing to write about.

Laura Bell was born in Scarborough, North Yorkshire. She studied Art Practice at Goldsmiths College, and currently lives and works between Paris and London. She lived for two years working as an artist on the Kent coast and worked on the Folkestone Trienniale.

Jay Bernard is a writer who draws. She's from London and was the Cityread 2013 writer in residence at the London Metropolitan Archives. In 2011/2012 she was academic fellow at the National University of Singapore. Her latest chapbook English Breakfast will be out later this year, and her first, Your Sign is Cuckoo, Girl is available from Tall Lighthouse. Jay has drawn and designed for publications such *Poetry Review*, *Wasafiri*, *MsLexia* and many a queer zine.

Owen Booth has worked as a copywriter, scriptwriter, journalist, bookseller, cocktail barman and content strategist. His work has been featured on BBC Radio and at the London Liars' League. Originally from Leeds, he lives in Walthamstow, East London.

Scott Brown works as a writer and editor for creative artists, craftspeople and culture professionals. He also makes stained glass windows, lives in France and is a somewhat obsessive walker. When asked about his creative writing, he might say something like this: 'All forms of art stitch a thread of fiction through the implausibility of reality, making the whole experience altogether more believable. And fun. I guess that's one reason why I like to write, and also why themes of place and creativity are often central to my work'.

Gary Budden is the co-founder of, and editor at, Influx Press. He works on editorial and events at *Ambit*. He grew up on the Kent coast in Whitstable, and lives in London.

Kit Caless is the publicist at Influx Press. He writes short stories and is currently working on a novel. He presents a literature show, 'Mapping the Metropolis' on Resonance 104.4FM. He also presents the breakfast show on Hackney radio station, NTS.

Daniel Cockrill is the founding member and host of BANG SAID THE GUN, the poetry event for people who don't necessarily like poetry. He has produced, directed, written and starred in various short poetry films for Channel 4 and has published two full collections of poetry entitled *Pie and Papier-Mâché* and *Cellotaping Rain To My Cheek*. He appears at numerous festivals and is a regular contributor on the 'Poetry Takeaway', the world's first mobile poetry emporium.

Rebecca Dawkins is 22 years old. She originates from and lives in Whitstable; her heart will forever belong to the Kentish coast. She graduated from Kent Uni in July 2012 and is now working her dream job at Random House publishing but can always find time for writing between the commuting, the job, her boyfriend, family and Parsons Jack Russell, Dennis (who rather likes the Kent coast too).

Travis Elborough is an author, broadcaster and cultural commentator. His books include *The Bus We Loved*, a history of the Routemaster bus; *The Long-Player Goodbye*, a hymn to vinyl records; and *Wish You Were Here,* a survey of the British beside the seaside. The most recent, *London Bridge in America: The Tall Story of a Transatlantic Crossing*, was published by Jonathan Cape in February 2013.

Salena Godden has been described as 'The doyenne of the spoken word scene' (Ian McMillan, BBC Radio 3's The Verb); 'The Mae West madam of the salon' (The Sunday Times) and as 'everything the Daily Mail is terrified of' (Kerrang! Magazine). She writes and performs poetry, fiction, memoir, radio drama and lyrics. Her most recent book of poems, *Under the Pier*, was published by Nasty Little Press in 2011. She is also known as The General of The Book Club Boutique, London's louchest literary salon, and as lead singer and lyricist of SaltPeter, alongside composer Peter Coyte. Her memoir, *Springfield Road* is being published by Unbound, a crowd funded publisher. Please visit www.unbound.co.uk.

James Arthur Jones is a mystery.

Steve Larder is an illustrator and author of the autobiographical comic-zine, *Rum Lad* and has been drawing ever since he can remember. His earliest memories include his grandmother tearing up cereal boxes to hand over the blank card on the inside, just so there was something to doodle on. Since then he hasn't stopped.

Rowena Macdonald was born on the Isle of Wight in 1974, grew up in the West Midlands and studied at the Universities of Sussex and Warwick. *Smoked Meat*, her debut book, was published by Flambard Press in 2011. In 2012 it was shortlisted for the Edge Hill Prize and longlisted for the Frank O'Connor Prize. Rowena works as a secretary at the House of Commons and teaches creative writing at Westminster University. She lives in east London but spends time in Newhaven, East Sussex, where her boyfriend works as a fisherman.

Ruth McDonald is a painter print-maker working from a studio in a Kentish copse. Her work portrays woodland landscape and the sea often illuminated by failing light and the moon and the traces left by past inhabitants. She constantly re-visits preferred sites in Kent and Cornwall to photograph and draw in-situ, then re-works and re-orders the images later in her sketchbook, subsequently produce drawings, paintings and prints. She describes an inner landscape where we can experience a sense of rhythmic energy and vitality in observation, reminding us of where we have come from and our ultimate destiny. An MA Graduate in Fine Art Ruth has exhibited in Kent, Cornwall, London, China and America. She also exhibits with The Earthbound Women, a Kent based group.

www.ruthmcdonald.co

www.earthboundwomen.co.uk

Madeleine McDonald lives on the east coast and writes columns on family life for the Yorkshire Post. History and tangled loyalties are recurrent themes in her other work, which has been published in anthologies or broadcast on local radio. Her first romance, *Enchantment in Morocco*, was published by http://www.redrosepublishing.com/.

Katrina Naomi is a poet based in south London and is originally from Margate. She is working towards a Creative Writing PhD at Goldsmiths, with a focus on violence in poetry. Her first full collection, *The Girl with the Cactus Handshake* (Templar Poetry), was shortlisted for the London New Poetry Award and received an Arts Council England writer's award.

Colin Priest upon graduating from the Architectural Association founded Studio Columba, an inter-disciplinary art and design practice based in Hackney Wick bridging areas of public performance, writing and intervention. In September 2010, he started an artistic experiment originating from his memory of childhood summers: *Greetings from*

DEAL and the making of collaborative multi-media narrative postcards, capturing intangible urban change with creative people connected to this unique place. In this time the project has evolved through Kent-centric conversations, various public exhibitions, generosities and shared ambitions of participants including; *Timeball 2012*, a Kent Cultural Baton commission and *Greetings from DEAL*: in Whitstable for the Satellite Whitstable Biennale 2012.

Adrian Self grew up in a number of cul-de-sacs, all of them circling the drain of London. He is graphic designer for an independent record label and lives in Sussex, where he plants more trees than he cuts down.

Chris Smisson is designer at Influx Press. He's from Kent, too.

Chimène Suleyman is a writer from London. With a background in performance poetry, she has represented the UK at the Internationale Biennale 2011. Her work considers the emptiness of the mundane; the loneliness, and appeal of, everyday nothingness.

Christian Watson is a writer. At night he sometimes tells his writing to strangers from a stage. Sometimes the stage is a bus stop. Christian would like to think that his work scathingly attacks a voyeuristic and misanthropic society addicted to the fantasy of violence doled out in increasingly spectacular media events, but admits if someone offered him one billion dollars to make a CGI reality gameshow sci-fi epic based on his writing, he would take it. The money would be spent wisely on pens, an AK-47 shaped swimming pool, and a security system so elaborate it would make Howard Hughes cry sterile tears of envy. Christian is currently studying English Literature at Chichester university. His poems and short stories have been published in various journals.

INFLUX
PRESS

Influx Press is an independent publisher that specialises in
short run, responsive fiction.

We publish challenging, controversial and alternative work that is
written in order to dissect and analyse our immediate surroundings
and produce site specific fiction and poetry.

Please visit

www.influxpress.com for extra material, including interviews

and videos with the authors.

Acquired for Development By...

A Hackney Anthology

....

Twenty-five writers, twenty-five different perspectives on the rapidly changing London Borough of Hackney. From gentrification to supermarket sandwiches, Turkish Alevism to inner-city river living, middle-class civil war to pylon romance *Acquired for Development By...* captures an alternative, insightful and sometimes bizarre take on modern London life.

....

'*A literary dolly mixture and a superb collection of original writing about London's most fascinating borough. This is Hackney without the hackneyed, and a must-read for anyone who cares about the area.*'

– The Londonist

Life in Transit

The Journey that Counts

Sam Berkson

....

Life in Transit searches for the public in a world that is increasingly privatised, both in terms of the 'chartered' space of corporate land grabs, but also the detachment of the individual in the late capitalist experience. Sam Berkson's collection focuses on the journey, rather than the destination.

....

'Berkson's own stories of life spent on London's public transport system bring political meanings to the tawdry and humdrum experience of the everyday commuter.'

– The *Independent*

Marshland

Dreams and Nightmares on the Edge of London

Gareth E Rees

Gareth Rees lives in Clapton, Hackney, with his wife and two daughters. He spends his days wandering the Lea Valley nature reserve with his trusty dog Hendrix, avoiding his family and the pressures of life. Out on the marsh he dwells among Victorian sewerage systems, dead toy factories, electricity pylons, and cows grazing in ancient pastures. Ghosts are his friends.

In a pre-historic landscape echoes of the future can be heard everywhere. Enter a liminal space of Olympic legacy, crocodile sightings, decapitated bears, Viking invasions and the hungry predations of property developers.